THE NEW YORK AQUARIUM
BOOK OF THE
WATER WORLD

THE NEW YORK AQUARIUM
BOOK OF THE

NEW YORK ZOOLOGICAL SOCIETY
AMERICAN HERITAGE PRESS • NEW YORK

WATER WORLD

A GUIDE TO REPRESENTATIVE FISHES, AQUATIC INVERTEBRATES, REPTILES, BIRDS, AND MAMMALS

WILLIAM BRIDGES CURATOR OF PUBLICATIONS EMERITUS
THE NEW YORK ZOOLOGICAL SOCIETY

Library of Congress Catalogue Card Number: 76-111654
SBN : 8281-0091-8 (paper)
        8281-0089-6 (cloth)

Black Sea Bass

INTRODUCTION

In an average year some seventeen million people visit aquariums in the United States. Obviously people are fascinated by fishes, to say nothing of other aquarium specialties such as those flowerlike animals called sea anemones, or the improbable octopus, or even the grotesque lobster.

It is a fascination that is hard to explain, but hardly needing explanation; we simply feel it. It is certainly not that we "identify" with a fish, as we might with a chimpanzee. The gap between us is too great for easy fellow feeling. Yet it is a gap we can at least partially bridge if we take the trouble to learn something about the fish's way of life. And it surely heightens our enjoyment of the water world if we realize that in many ways its inhabitants are not so very different from us. They have their problems, too. We superior human beings are not alone in having enemies and diseases and in needing to eat to keep alive. We worry about polluted air, but seldom actually die of it; fishes *do* die of polluted water.

The New York Aquarium Book of the Water World is intended for people who have curiosity and questions about the living creatures of the sea and of freshwater streams and ponds, of lakes and marshes and swamps, and of the brackish interzone between salt and fresh water. Fishes are perhaps foremost in our concern, for they most often come into our lives via the frying pan or sport or the home aquarium. But also sharing our interest are the bewildering variety of animals without backbones, the invertebrates; higher up in the scale, the amphibians that lead a double life in water and on land; and finally the reptiles and birds and mammals most closely associated with water.

Nobody knows exactly how many species of fish there are in the world. A number often cited is twenty thousand, and more are being discovered and named every year. As for the aquatic invertebrates — jellyfishes and clams, shrimps and crabs and lobsters, corals and octopuses, sea stars and sea anemones and sponges, to name but a few familiar ones — a fair estimate is 120,-000 species, not including one-celled animals and insects. The amphibians (salamanders, toads, frogs) exist in some three thousand species, sea turtles in five (plus 206 other turtles, many of which are more or less at home in the water), crocodilians in twenty-one, and the sea snakes in about fifty. Altogether there are about 2,125 species of snake, a good many of which live in, or take readily to, fresh water. There is even an aquatic lizard, the Marine Iguana of the Galápagos Islands.

Mammals have developed as essentially terrestrial animals, and today there are only 136 of the so-called aquatic species. Many birds, of course, depend on sea and fresh water for food, but the seventeen species of penguin are the most water-bound. They nest on land, but the sea is their real home; flightless, they are propelled by flipperlike wings so that they seem to "fly" underwater.

So vast is the water world that none of us can do more than sample it. This we can do most generously in a public aquarium where techniques and apparatus are available to keep alive a widely representative variety of creatures from the other world of water. More intimately and personally, but to a limited extent, we can sense the wonder and beauty of aquatic life through the home aquarium hobby. But however we approach it, there is no denying the appeal of the water world.

For general direction and constant advice, the author of *The New York Aquarium Book of the Water World* is indebted to Ross F. Nigrelli, Director of the Osborn Laboratories of Marine Sciences, and to Robert A. Morris, Curator of the Aquarium. Assistant Curator U. Erich Friese was of invaluable assistance to photographer Bill Meng by setting up special exhibits for photography.

CONTENTS

AQUARIUMS: GATEWAYS
TO THE WATER WORLD

Someday our major cities may have moon museums of tiny craters and lunar debris rocketed back to earth in space ships. But here and now we already have museums of another world. We call them aquariums.

For water *is* another world. We are air people, and aquatic animals are creatures of the water world, *in* another world we can penetrate only briefly and provisionally. And if we think of an aquarium as a water museum, its exhibits are surely stranger and more beautiful and possessed of more enduring mystery than any lifeless detritus pried out of the moon.

When you visit a public aquarium — and there are many great ones, not only in the United States, but all over the world — think of it as a water museum. Or, if you prefer, think of it as a gateway through which you enter into a world of ceaseless motion and deep quiescence, of bizarre forms and obscure devices, and of colors and harmonies you will never forget.

People have been keeping fishes in confinement for a long, long time. The Sumerians stocked ponds and pools with food fishes as far back as 2500 B.C., and among the "firsts" with which China must be credited was the domestication of carp more than two thousand years ago; the Chinese may also be said to have pioneered the home-aquarium hobby, for they were developing fancy goldfish and carp during the Sung dynasty (960–1278) and were the first to keep them indoors in porcelain vessels. This was purely for the pleasure of fish-watching, a pleasure that knows no territorial boundaries. As the advertising booklet of the Japanese Fancy Carp Cultivation Association puts it, "It is a common joy for adults as well as children to be comforted with these colorful, innocent fancy carp after a day of hard work or study."

Goldfish and carp are freshwater fishes, of course, but marine fishes also have a long history of captivity; the ancient Romans penned them in pools connected with the sea and are known to have kept them as pets.

Oddly enough, although zoological parks more or less as we know them today have existed for more than two thousand years, it never seems to have occurred to anyone to put a representative collection of fishes on public exhibition until the middle of the last century. In the spring of 1853 the Zoological Society of London opened a "Fish House" in its garden in Regent's Park. It was nowhere as elaborate as the public aquariums of today—merely a number of standing glass aquariums in a conservatory-like building—but it did show both saltwater and freshwater fishes. The exhibit was enormously successful and set off a craze for keeping fishes in homes all over England.

A modern public aquarium: the New York Aquarium, beside the sea at Coney Island, New York City

America, which had borrowed so much from Europe, was slow to sense the charm of looking at fishes. There were tem-

porary fish exhibitions in this country from time to time—the World's Columbian Exposition in 1893 had an extremely popular one—but it was not until December 10, 1896, when the New York Aquarium was opened, that the United States had a permanent public aquarium. Now there are about one hundred—not all public, in the sense that they are operated by a municipality or a nonprofit organization, but permanent exhibitions nevertheless, and many of them important in aquatic research.

Research is, indeed, almost an inescapable part of an aquarium's operation, for there is so much we need to know about the lives of fishes if we are to keep them successfully. Hence the collateral development of marine biological stations, such as the one in Naples that was opened in 1874, that of the Marine Biological

Association of the United Kingdom at Plymouth in Devonshire, and the Osborn Laboratories of Marine Sciences in New York. Their research extends far beyond the mere techniques of exhibition and may be involved with the biology of fishes, the problems of commercial fisheries, or the concept of the sea as a source not only of food for mankind but of biochemical substances of potentially even greater importance. As an example, in the Osborn Laboratories the genetics of cancer in fishes, the isolation of antibiotics from marine organisms, and the adhesive secretions of barnacles are only three of many lines of investigation being carried out. In fact, as the Co-ordinator of Research has written, the Laboratories are "concerned with the wide gamut of the sea — from studies on the micronutrients at the base of the food chain to the most highly developed marine mammals. The Laboratories have been specifically designed for . . . pathology, microbiology, physiology, pharmacology, bio-organic chemistry, virology, tissue culture, embryology and teratology, pollution, planktonology, radiobiology, genetics and vertebrate biology."

"Every schoolboy knows that water is H_2O and every aquarium man wishes that were all it is," an aquarium man wrote some years ago. It was a cry from the heart, for aquarium men are obsessed by water, its management, its movement, its temperature and salinity and alkalinity and chemical balance. Not all aquarium exhibits are intolerant of water not "natural" to them — sea lions and penguins, for instance, get along perfectly well in fresh water instead of the sea water in which they normally live. But most marine fishes and invertebrates are not so accommodating; they simply die if their accustomed conditions are not met. Sea water itself is an extremely complex substance containing sixty-seven chemical elements, and so corrosive is its action that no metal apparatus — pumps and pipes — can be allowed to come into contact with it. Many fishes are highly susceptible to poisoning by dissolved metals; some marine fishes, for example, die if only one part per million of copper gets into their water. Consequently aquariums use polyvinyl chloride, an inert plastic, or hard rubber or transite in their apparatus for moving water.

The practicability of making acceptable sea water from fresh water by the addition of certain chemicals is now so well established that even quite large inland aquariums are able to maintain outstanding marine exhibits. Institutions close beside the sea would seem to have no problems at all — you just pump water out of the ocean, and let the overflow from your tanks spill back into the ocean. Actually it is not that simple. The local sea water may be polluted or cloudy or of fluctuating temperature, for instance. The Van Kleef Aquarium in Singapore found it could not use the local sea water. "We are in the middle of the Sunda Plateau," the Director wrote, "with shallow sea in all directions, heated through by the tropical sun and diluted by the enormous rainfall. Many common Indo-Pacific species avoid these waters, and even our indigenous fishes find them hard to tolerate in confined conditions. So we model our water on that of the Indian Ocean off Ceylon." This they do by means of a closed circulation involving great reservoirs where the water can be conditioned to an established ideal.

To take another example, the New York Aquarium met the problem in a different way. When it was first opened at Coney Island, a few hundred feet from the Atlantic, pipes were extended into the ocean to just below the low-tide mark, and sea water was pumped into the tanks from shallow well-points. The pipes were soon clogged by sand, mussels, and other marine organisms, turbidity was high, and there were intolerable seasonal variations in temperature. Eventually it was found that beautifully pure, clear sea water at a constant temperature of 53° F could be extracted from two deep wells just outside the Aquarium's walls. The wells were sunk to a depth of 200 feet to tap an aquifer, or water-bearing stratum in the sand, and each yields about four hundred gallons a minute at a constant, year-round temperature.

Nothing in an aquarium can be taken for granted—especially not the water. The entire water system must be checked for its content of oxygen and carbon dioxide, nitrates and phosphates; for the nitrites and ammonia that are poisonous to fishes; for acidity and alkalinity (pH); for temperature and salinity.

The business of maintaining the right kind of water, salt or fresh, is only one preoccupation of an aquarium's staff, however. Providing an ever-changing, ever-growing show is another. Not that people get tired of seeing "the same old fish," but every aquarium man likes to offer variety and meet the challenge of a species he has never shown before. Or to breed them, if possible. As one aquarium man wrote, "The greatest compliment animals can pay an aquarist is to breed in his tanks."

Aquatic animals the world over come from five principal sources. Expeditions in quest of specific marine mammals or general collections of certain kinds of fishes are one source, and may take collecting crews to the Arctic or the Antarctic, to Bermuda, Florida, or almost any other place in the world. It is sometimes rough-and-tumble work, too, for it is not easy to net a Killer Whale, or to haul a Walrus pup into a small boat in stormy seas, or to rope a threshing 700-pound White Whale in shallow water.

The worldwide network of airlines has greatly diversified aquarium collections by making the exchange of local fishes comparatively easy. Fishes travel well in sealed plastic bags of water and oxygen and in two or three days can be delivered virtually anywhere in the world. Aquariums in regions where beautifully colored fishes are commonplace, such as the Indo-Pacific, can ship brilliant prizes to other institutions and receive in return comparable local fishes. Even such large creatures as sharks can be transported by air in sealed water tanks.

Animal dealers who specialize in supplying fishes do an enormous business with the home-aquarium trade, of course, but are important to large public aquariums, too, for they are often able to supply exotic fishes and invertebrates. Indeed, a number of the most beautiful fishes come not from the open ocean but from "fish farms" such as those in Florida.

Aquariums along the seashore need look no further than their own "back yards" for a surprising variety of fishes. Even along the coast of the North Atlantic many young tropical marine fishes are found in summer, and oceanside aquariums are likely to have their own collecting boats to harvest them. Or they may make regular visits to trawlers and pound nets to select local fishes from the catches.

Birth is the least common method of acquiring fish for exhibition, for eggs and fry seldom have much chance of developing in tanks where the population of other fishes is more concentrated than it would be in a stream, pond, or the ocean; for that matter, mortality of eggs and fry is very high even in the open sea. The marine mammals have a much better record, and births of sea lions and various seals are not uncommon.

Catering for a collection of perhaps several hundred species requires certain more or less standard food items: mackerel, herring, smelts, butterfish, squid, clams, shrimp, tubifex worms, dry foods, and (for seahorses and some butterflyfish) those tiny, jerkily swimming organisms known as brine shrimp. Oddly enough, there is usually little preying on other living creatures in the same tank; if food is plentifully supplied, why work to get it?

That is not to say that all inhabitants of the tanks do not relish an occasional snack—there are records of lobsters that liked to nibble on the plywood walls of their tank.

Aquarium housekeeping is never-ending. Food preparation is almost constant. Outdoor tanks for marine mammals must be emptied and scrubbed frequently, and algae must be routinely scrubbed off the glass fronts of the tanks. Dead corals used as tank decorations and as hiding places for fishes must occasionally be taken out and bleached. Water-management problems, the transfer and replacement of specimens, and a dozen other chores keep aquarium staffs busy around the clock. No aquarium "just happens."

OUTSTANDING AQUARIUMS
OF THE WORLD

Nearly four hundred public aquariums are listed in the *Directory of Public Aquaria of the World*, issued by the Waikiki Aquarium in Honolulu. Japan alone has seventy-six—a surprisingly large number for such a small country. A short check list of the larger aquariums is given here for the convenience of travelers who—once they are "hooked" on fishes—may like to know where they can indulge their hobby of fish-watching.

Austria
  Aquarium des Tiergartens Schönbrunn, Vienna
Bermuda
  Bermuda Government Aquarium, The Flatts
Canada
  Vancouver Public Aquarium, Vancouver, British Columbia
  Montreal Aquarium, Montreal
Denmark
  Danmarks Akvarium, Charlottenlund
England
  The Aquarium, Plymouth
  Zoological Society of London, London
France
  Aquarium, Roscoff, Finisterre
  Aquarium du Laboratoire Arago, Banyuls-sur-Mer
Germany (East)
  Terrarium & Aquarium, Berlin
Germany (West)
  Wilhelmina, Stuttgart, Baden-Württemberg
  Berliner Aquarium, Berlin
  Exotarium, Frankfurt
  Aquarium Köln, Cologne
Italy
  Stazione Zoologica Aquario, Naples
  Aquario, Messina
Japan
  Enoshima Aquarium and Marineland, Fujisawa

Fukuoka Aquarium, Hakazaki, Fukuoka
Miyajima Aquarium, Hiroshima
Nagasaki Aquarium, Nagasaki
Shimonoseki Aquarium, Shimonoseki
Suma Aquarium, Kobe
Yomiuriland Marine Aquarium, Kawasaki
Monaco
Aquarium du Musée Oceanographique, Monaco
Netherlands
Artis-Aquarium, Amsterdam
New Caledonia
Aquarium de Nouméa, Nouméa
Norway
Bergen Aquarium, Bergen
Portugal
Aquario Vasco da Gama, Lisbon
Singapore
Van Kleef Aquarium
South Africa
Centenary Aquarium, Durban
East London Aquarium, East London
Sweden
Malmö Akvariet, Malmö
Switzerland
Aquarium, Basel
Aquarium, Zurich
United States
Point Defiance Aquarium, Tacoma, Washington
Marine World, San Francisco, California
Steinhart Aquarium, San Francisco, California
Marineland of the Pacific, Palos Verdes, California
T. Wayland Vaughn Aquarium, La Jolla, California
Sea World, San Diego, California
Sea Life Park, Waimanalo, Hawaii
Waikiki Aquarium, Honolulu, Hawaii
John G. Shedd Aquarium, Chicago, Illinois
The Cleveland Aquarium, Cleveland, Ohio
New England Aquarium, Boston, Massachusetts
New York Aquarium, Brooklyn, New York
Aquarium of Niagara Falls, Niagara Falls, New York
Pittsburgh Aquarium, Pittsburgh, Pennsylvania
Marineland of Florida, St. Augustine, Florida
Ocean World, Inc., Fort Lauderdale, Florida
Miami Seaquarium, Miami, Florida
The Dallas Aquarium, Dallas, Texas
Sea-Arama, Galveston, Texas

FISHES

I f fishes were not so common or many of them so familiar, we might esteem them above most other living creatures. For among them are tiny jewels and overwhelming monsters, slender perfection of form and muscled corpulence, the bizarre and the beautiful and the mysterious, all attuned by delicacies of response to a world largely alien to us — prisoners of that world for the most part, but becoming more and more accessible to our minutest study and enjoyment and use.

But they *are* common; nearly half of the estimated 41,200 species of backboned animals of the world today are fishes. As for the number of individuals . . . figures lose their meaning when millions are piled upon millions and more millions. It is estimated that at least sixty-four million tons of fish are caught every year for food — and the catch is increasing at an annual rate of 8 per cent.

Only the birds, possessing the ocean of air, have a larger dominion, for the waters cover more than 70 per cent of the earth, and where there is water, there fishes are likely to be found, whether it be the warm shallows of the tropical seas, the all but freezing waters of Antarctica, the cold black abyss of mid-ocean or on the bottom 6 miles down, stagnant swamps and sparkling mountain streams, warm springs, lakes, ponds, rivers, creeks, the underground waters in caves. In short, the estimated twenty thousand species of fish have adapted themselves to almost every variation of their water environment since they took form more than 450 million years ago, the first backboned life to appear on earth. Only mammals are more versatile, and man most so, for he can carry his environment with him in mechanical devices.

Water is some eight hundred times denser than air, and this fact determines the general form of active fishes; the sleek, streamlined form of a trout permits it to dart at a speed of about five miles an hour, the powerfully muscled Bluefin Tuna at an astonishing forty-four miles an hour. These maximum speeds cannot, of course, be maintained for long; for most it is a matter of seconds.

But not all fishes are active, and their way of life is reflected in their form; efficient streamlining would be useless to a bottom-grubbing catfish, a venom-bearing Scorpionfish, or a deep-sea anglerfish.

How fishes swim — move forward, backward, up, and down — has been the subject of elaborate study for many years. There is no uniform method. In some it is by repeated flexure of the body; others are mainly or entirely propelled by the fins (those of seahorses oscillate up to seventy times a second); usually there is some combination of these methods.

To stay in one place, to hover, as a sunfish does over its nest, or to maintain a head-down position, as the Headstanders do, is as complex a maneuver as swimming, for living water is never dead still, and even if it were, the mere drawing in of water through the mouth and its expulsion through the gills would give some forward motion to the fish's body — a minute application of the jet-engine principle. Every slightest eddy and current must be counteracted by precise and delicate motions of the fins.

But swimming is not the only way fishes have evolved of getting somewhere else; they soar, crawl, climb, leap, hop, burrow, and employ jet propulsion. A spectacular example of one of these methods is furnished by the flyingfishes of tropical and warm oceans, often observed from the decks of ships. Their techniques have been analyzed by high-speed photography. By the time the fish is ready to leave the water, it is swimming at fifteen to twenty miles an hour, its tail beating fiercely at some fifty strokes a second, the body angled up at 15 degrees, and the large pectoral fins extended like wings. Once airborne, other fins may be extended, the fish "levels off," the tail leaves the water like an airplane breaking contact with the runway, and the fish soars. Sometimes, like a practicing pilot making "touch and go" landings and takeoffs, the fish may drop down and dip its tail into the water, beating it to renew speed, then soar again for as many as five successive flights. Glides have been timed for up to ten seconds, and a succession may carry a fish several hundred yards.

Quite a number of fishes use paired fins as limbs for crawling over the bottom. The Sargassumfish works its leisurely way through the tangled jungle of Sargassum weed by grasping and hauling with its fins. And the small, goggle-eyed Mudskipper of the brackish shore waters of Africa, Asia, and Australia uses its fins and flicking motions of its tail to walk on mud flats and mangrove roots with complete nonchalance. The common Eel, as is well known, may travel considerable distances overland from some isolated pond to a flowing stream when making its migration to spawn in the ocean, using snakelike motions of its body.

Water is not only denser than air, it is buoyant; and fishes with gasbladders are actually weightless in water, much like a man in space (although for a different reason). On the other hand, a shark or a darter, lacking a gasbladder, would sink if it did not swim.

This gas-filled sac called a gasbladder mainly serves the purpose of maintaining buoyancy, but some fishes use it as a lung, and in others it has a connection with the ears and is used to pick up sounds or to transmit them. Gas is absorbed or excreted into it to compensate for changes in pressure, and thus at a given level the sac maintains buoyancy. Some fishes charge it by gulping air at the surface, others secrete gases from the bloodstream; a Goldfish, for instance, may take five to seven days to secrete enough to charge an empty gasbladder.

As fishes pump water through their gills, dissolved oxygen becomes available to them. But what about fishes that live in swamps, where the dissolved oxygen content of the water is very low? Here fishes may be adapted for gulping air from above the surface or for drawing in water from just below the surface film, where the proportion of dissolved oxygen is highest. The familiar Guppy is very good at this sort of thing. Lungfishes can take in gulps of air—the African and South American species get 95 per cent of their oxygen in that way—but the Australian Lungfish depends on its gills except when the water is stagnant.

The dramatic lives and encounters of predatory fishes may lead to the impression that all fishes live by eating one another, as communities are said to live by taking in one another's washing. The food chain actually starts far below the fish-eat-fish level with microscopically small green plants and minute animals called respectively, phytoplankton and zooplankton. Some quite sizable fishes feed for their entire lives on these organisms, others do so only when they are very young and small. Of course, many fishes feed on both plants and animals, but at the top of the food chain—or, better still, the food pyramid—are the carnivores, the predators that fatten on other fishes (which may themselves be predators), as well as on any more exotic meat they can capture or find. Fishermen have reported finding mice, snakes, and turtles in the stomach of a bass, for instance.

Size does not determine whether a given fish is a meateater or a plankton-eater; for example, in northern waters the huge Basking Shark, sometimes 45 feet long, subsists entirely on zooplankton, and in winter, when the plankton supply is at low ebb, it sinks to the bottom and lies cold and torpid until the feeding season starts again and it rises to bask at the surface.

Any fish is potential prey if its sphere of life lies within that of the predators, but fishes have many and ingenious ways of protecting themselves—spines that are certainly sharp and in some are venomous, camouflage by color or form or matching of backgrounds, armored skin and scales, mimicry of other fishes that are more immune to attack for some reason, the emission of obscuring clouds of ink (or even luminous matter in some deep-sea fishes), discharge of electricity. And, of course, there is speed of escape, although the predators are likely to be speedy themselves. Even "schooling," in which large numbers of the same kind of fish swim and feed together, has its protective aspects. One of the most curious adaptations is that by which anemonefishes take refuge among the stinging tentacles of sea amenones and are unharmed by them.

In a world in which there are so many hazards from predators and diseases, as well as the necessity of perfect adjustment to small variations in habitat, the sense organs of fishes must be acute. They are. Most ray-finned fishes have a sense of color — some more sensitive than that of man — but vision is probably limited to about 50 feet in even the clearest water. Those in the blackness of the great ocean depths, far below the limits of marine twilight, have small eyes that nevertheless may make them aware of the luminescence of other fishes. Fishes' hearing is generally good, sometimes more acute than that of human beings. Sharks and eels have an especially highly developed sense of smell.

Sight, smell, hearing, taste, touch — man has all these senses, however well or poorly developed in comparison with fishes — but the lateral line, a sensitive streak along the sides of many fishes, is peculiar to fishes. It has been described as a "distant touch" device to detect pressure waves generated by a moving object — such as another fish — or the distortion of the fish's own "bow wave" as it approaches a fixed object. This sensory system is scattered over the body in sharks and lampreys and in some minnows, instead of being concentrated in the lateral line. Some fishes without eyes get along quite well by means of the sensitivity of this lateral line.

Thanks mainly to the hydrophone, we now know that the underwater world is not one of eternal silence; in fact, it is decidedly noisy. Fishes make sounds that have been described as grunts, groans, squeaks, snores, purrs, or whistles, as drumming, humming, growling, or hissing, and some African fishermen locate schools of fish by inserting a three-pronged pole into the water and rotating it slowly with the ear held against the shaft. In some ways water is a better conductor of sound than air is, and even faint sounds may be detected — for instance, when a school of anchovy makes an abrupt turn. Some fishes make sounds by "grinding their teeth," others by friction of bones in the pectoral-fin arch, the sounds being resonated by the gasbladder. Drumfishes are especially noisy, and the toadfish can give off deafening growling-grunts, both fishes by vibrating their gasbladders with muscles specially developed for that purpose. Sounds serve various purposes: claiming a territory (like song in birds), courtship, locating others of the same kind, and the like.

The intricacies of fishes could be discussed endlessly, but many of these will emerge in the accounts of specific fishes.[1] Here it is enough to give only the broad dictionary definition of a fish:

Any of numerous cold-blooded, strictly aquatic, water-breathing craniate vertebrates having the limbs (when present) developed as fins, and typically a long, scaly, somewhat tapering body ending in a broad, vertical caudal fin.

And to add that a dictionary definition doesn't tell the whole story, by any means!

---

[1] In the section that follows, the classification of fishes is in the main that of L. S. Berg (1940).

Sharks
ORDER SQUALIFORMES

Sharks and their relatives, the skates, rays, and chimaeras, are called "cartilage fishes" because their skeletons are composed of cartilage instead of bone. Some 250 species of shark are found in temperate and tropical seas around the world, but only about a dozen are known to attack man. Two with especially bad reputations are the White Shark, up to 36½ feet long, sometimes reported along the Pacific and Atlantic coasts of the United States, and the Hammerhead, also known in our waters along both coasts.

Hungry sharks are sometimes said to eat anything, and indeed, remains of water birds, porpoises, dogs, sea turtles, stingrays, other sharks, tin cans, coal, and even parts of a bicycle have been found in shark stomachs. All sharks are meat-eaters, but the docile Whale Shark—largest of all fishes, reputed to reach a length of 50 feet and a weight of 25 tons—feeds on small zooplankton, schools of little fishes, and squids. It lives in all tropical seas.

See page 25

Some sharks lay eggs that become leathery in the water, the young emerging after several months. Most of them bring forth their young alive. A litter of eighty-two has been recorded for the Tiger Shark of tropical and occasionally temperate waters; the Sand Shark found in our area, as well as in Australia and South Africa, has but two young in each brood.

Sand Shark with Sharksucker on its back

Sharkskin leather has some economic value, and during World War II there was a demand for the vitamin-rich oil obtained from shark livers until synthetic vitamins replaced it. The Soupfin Shark of the Pacific American coast finds a market, and that popular British institution, fish and chips, depends largely upon shark flesh.

Horn Sharks
SQUALIFORMES: HETERODONTIDAE

Horn sharks are so called from the heavy spine on the forward edge of the two dorsal fins. They are found in most tropical and temperate waters except the Atlantic and the Mediterranean, and there are about ten species.

The Horn Shark that ranges from southern California south into the Gulf of California has a peculiarly piglike "face" and is sometimes called the Pig Shark. Eggs are about 4 by 2 inches, dark and cylindrical, and the 8-inch young hatch in about seven months.

Sand Sharks
SQUALIFORMES: CARCHARIIDAE

The Sand Shark that ranges along the coast from Maine to Florida is not a man-killer in these waters, but it certainly looks as if it were: the crescentic mouth and fearsome array of teeth are almost a cartoonist's caricature of "sharkiness." There are some six species on both sides of the Atlantic, in the Mediter- *Whale Shark*

ranean, and along the coasts of Argentina, Australia, Japan, China, and India. There are records of attacks on swimmers off Australia.

Lacking a gasbladder, Sand Sharks gulp air that is held in the stomach, and the stomach thus serves to maintain buoyancy. The two young are born alive.

Sand Sharks adapt well to captivity and have lived as long as nine years in the New York Aquarium.

Mackerel Sharks
SQUALIFORMES: LAMNIDAE

As late as the middle years of this century some scientists were reluctant to believe that sharks attacked human beings; at best they conceded that attacks were extremely rare. Certainly sharks are not an everyday hazard, even in Australian waters where there are adequate records for about one hundred attacks spread over forty years. Nevertheless, some sharks *are* a hazard, and a special Shark Research Panel set up by the American Institute of Biological Sciences in the 1950's has abundant records to prove it.

See page 26

Among the so-called mackerel sharks, the White Shark of all tropical and temperate seas is commonly known as the Maneater and is the most dangerous of all sharks. It was an 8½-foot White

Tiger Shark.
PERRY W. GILBERT
PHOTO.

Smooth Dogfish

Lemon Shark feeding on a Blue Marlin.
PERRY W. GILBERT
PHOTO.

Dusky Shark of the Atlantic. (Carcharhinidae).
PERRY W. GILBERT
PHOTO.

25

White Shark, or Maneater.
WOMETCO MIAMI SEAQUARIUM PHOTO.

Shark that terrorized the New Jersey coast in the summer of 1916, killing four men and boys and mutilating another boy. It has been seen as far north as Newfoundland.

The speedy Mako Shark, dark blue above and white below, is sometimes taken in seining operations off New York. A little over 10 feet long, it is dangerous, but not a consistent man-killer.

Few generalizations can be made about sharks; the highly experienced underwater explorer Jacques-Yves Cousteau commented that "one can never tell what a shark is going to do." However, records show that sharks rarely attack in water cooler than 65° F and that blood in the water helps put them in a feeding mood.

Nurse Sharks
SQUALIFORMES: ORECTOLOBIDAE

Although the Nurse Shark reaches a length of 14 feet, it is *See page 24* not ordinarily dangerous unless provoked, and its usual food is mollusks, crustaceans, and small fishes. It ranges from the Florida Keys (occasionally up to North Carolina) through the West Indies to Brazil and along the west coast of Africa. Other nurse sharks of some two dozen species are found in Indo-Pacific waters.

Not all nurse sharks are harmless, however; in Australian waters, where they are called Wobbegongs, attacks have occurred.

Requiem Sharks
SQUALIFORMES: CARCHARHINIDAE

This is the largest family of sharks. Its members are not regularly exhibited in glass-sided aquarium tanks—for some reason they do not thrive there, although they can be kept more easily in opaque-sided pools—but this disability is gradually being overcome, and the impressive Lemon Shark is exhibited with in- *See page 25* creasing frequency. It is an inshore species, common in enclosed bays and sounds and river mouths from New Jersey to northern Brazil, and is plentiful enough in waters around Florida and the Keys. It reaches a maximum length of 11 feet.

Like others of its family, it can be dangerous, and there is at least one recorded incident of an unprovoked attack on a swimmer.

Lobster fishermen have few kind words to say for the Smooth Dogfish; the food of this small shark is chiefly crusta- *See page 25* ceans, and since it is sometimes extremely abundant inshore from Cape Cod to Brazil, it is a serious predator on the lobsters that man would rather reserve for himself. It is found on both sides of the Atlantic.

Five feet is its maximum length, and small specimens are often used for classroom dissection. Normally grayish olive above and yellowish below, it has the ability to change color—slowly, over a period of two days—and may take on a pearly tint when it is over a pale sand bottom. The young are born alive.

One of the most striking of the carcharhinids is the Leopard Shark, yellow with strong dark bands on its back. It is found from Oregon to Lower California and is often exhibited in other parts of the world because of the ease with which it can be transported by air in sealed bags of oxygen and water.

A fairly common summer visitor in the Atlantic from Maine to Long Island is the Blue Shark, a 12-foot-long, very slender shark that is almost indigo blue above and white below. It keeps mostly to deep water, and although it has been photographed (from a cage) off Montauk Point on Long Island, it has never been much of a hazard to swimmers.

Hammerhead Sharks
SQUALIFORMES: SPHYRNIDAE

Young Smooth Hammerhead Sharks are fairly common in the New York region in summer, and although they may be only about 2 feet long (adults reach 17 feet), they make spectacular exhibits because of their peculiar "hammer-shaped" head with the eyes and nostrils at the end of the broad wings, which are a yard wide in adults.

Hammerheads are definitely in the group of man-killers. One scientist, confessing that the function of the broad head and offset eyes and nostrils had never been satisfactorily explained, surmised that the nasal groove along the front of the head might give them an advantage in smelling blood or prey. "At any rate," he wrote, "hammerheads are usually the first, or among the first, to arrive at the scene of bloodshed."

Hammerheads are found in all tropical seas, moving into temperate waters only in the summer. Their usual food is fish and squids.

Spiny Dogfishes
SQUALIFORMES: SQUALIDAE

One member of this family should be well known to anyone who has taken a college zoology course: the Spiny Dogfish. Reeking of formalin, it is a common introduction to the mysteries of dissection. Its abundance along the American Atlantic coast from Nova Scotia to North Carolina is one reason for its classroom use. Commercial fishermen dislike it because of its destructiveness to food fish and because quantities are caught for which there is no market.

The Spiny Dogfish is usually less than 3½ feet in length and is grayish in color. The young, up to eleven, are born alive.

Skates and Rays
ORDER RAJIFORMES

This large order includes sawfishes, guitarfishes, electric rays, skates, stingrays, eagle rays, and mantas, or devilrays, and some of the approximately 340 species are found in most tropical or temperate seas. Characteristically they are flattened, and the broad pectoral fins are attached to the head, giving them a rather triangular appearance. Many have whiplike tails.

Species that feed on the bottom have their gills on the underside of the pectoral fins, drawing in water through spiracles at the top of the head and expelling it through the gills. Those that do not live on the bottom take water in through the mouth in the usual manner.

Electric rays of all temperate and tropical oceans can give off as many as 200 volts. Stingrays have venomous spines on the upper surface of the tail near its base, as do some of the mantas. The Atlantic Manta, the largest, is sometimes 22 feet across the "wings."

Sawfishes
RAJIFORMES: PRISTIDAE

The sawfishes of the world's warm seas look as if they would be extremely dangerous, for the flat snout with its double edge of teeth may be 6 feet long and a foot broad at the base; the sawfish may be 35 feet long overall and weigh up to 2½ tons. Actually it is not aggressive, and the saw is used to dig in the bottom sand and to kill or disable prey, as when it is swished rapidly from side to side in a school of fish. There are about six species.

The Smalltooth Sawfish of the western Atlantic, like other sawfishes, enters brackish and even fresh water and is often caught in the Indian River in Florida. The young are born alive, and at birth the saw is soft. *See page 31*

Electric Rays
RAJIFORMES: TORPEDINIDAE

Two electric rays are found in the North Atlantic, the Lesser Electric Ray and the Atlantic Torpedo, and while neither gives off the tremendous jolt of an Electric Eel, they should be respected. The electric organs are in the "wings" next to the head.

Electric rays are known in all tropical and temperate oceans, and some can discharge 200 volts. Fortunately they are nowhere very numerous and are not dangerous unless unwisely handled; they feed mainly on small fish.

The boldly spotted Lesser Electric Ray is commoner from North Carolina southward than in New York waters, but it is occasionally taken in the New York area. It is about 2 feet long. The Atlantic Torpedo, found from Maine to Cuba, may be 5 feet long and has proportionately heavier discharges of electricity. The discharge is used both for capture of prey and for defense. *See page 31*

Skates
RAJIFORMES: RAJIDAE

Anyone who has done much wandering on the beaches between Nova Scotia and South Carolina is likely to have seen egg cases of the skates, dark and leathery rectangles with a spiny hook at each corner. These egg cases, which lie on the bottom during incubation, more or less anchored by bits of stone and shell that adhere to their sticky threads, are often called "mermaids' purses."

The Little Skate, only about 20 inches long and weighing just above a pound, is one of the commonest of the forty-odd species of skate along the Atlantic coast. It is also called the Hedgehog Skate, from the spines on the upper surface of the body.

See page 32

The Clearnose Skate is another common species along the Atlantic coast from Maine to Florida, although it is not so numerous at the extremes of its range. It reaches a length of about 2 feet and feeds on crustaceans and small fish.

Stingrays
RAJIFORMES: DASYATIDAE

Stingrays are dangerous and should be treated with respect whenever they are encountered, for most of the approximately 118 species have a sharp, venom-bearing spine on the upper surface of the tail. Those with long and whiplike tails may switch the tail from side to side, or flick it forward over the head, with such force that the spine .can penetrate a wooden boat. The largest member of the family is an Australian species more than 6 feet across the wings and weighing 750 pounds; the smallest is the little Yellow Stingray of the West Indies and the southern shores of the United States that is seldom more than 1 foot long. Deaths have occurred from abdominal or chest wounds inflicted by large stingrays.

Stingrays have powerful grinding teeth capable of crushing clamshells. The young are born alive.

The Roughtail Stingray, sometimes as long as 12 feet, but more usually up to 6 feet, lives along the shore from Maine to Cape Hatteras and is more plentiful in the southern part of its range.

Another well-known species is the Bluntnose Stingray, found from the Carolinas southward and common in Florida waters. Adults are olive brown, and the young are reddish or yellowish.

Eagle Rays, Cow-nosed Rays
RAJIFORMES: MYLIOBATIDAE

Most of the approximately thirty species in this family of eagle rays, bat rays, and cow-nosed rays of most tropical and temperate seas carry a venomous spine on the trailing, whiplike tail, so that handling even a young one is no job for an amateur. The young are born alive, descending tailfirst from the female's body, and the spine at this time is soft and flexible; it hardens rapidly on exposure to sea water, and in a few days the baby can flick his tail forward and to either side in a no-nonsense manner.

Smalltooth Sawfish

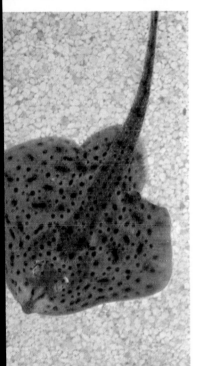

LEFT: *Little Skate*
RIGIIT: *Lesser
Electric Ray*

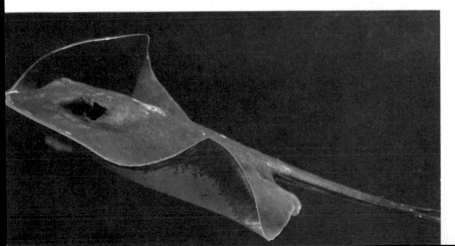

Roughtail Stingray

31

Cow-nosed Rays

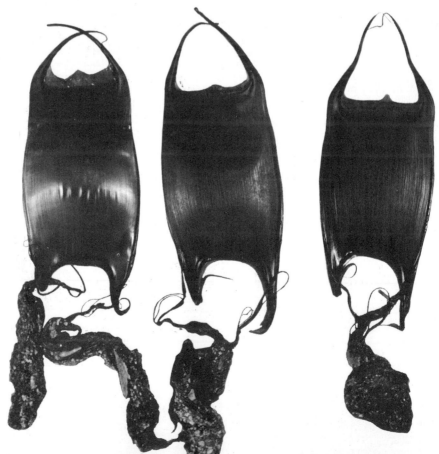

*Egg cases of
Clearnose Skate*

32

These rays swim by a steady up-and-down motion of the "wings," the broad pectoral fins, and can soar, swirl, or glide with seemingly effortless ease. They feed on almost anything that comes along, from crabs and lobsters and small fish to clams and oysters; indeed, commercial beds of clams and oysters on the Pacific coast of North America have been protected from the Bat Stingray by palisades of stout posts.

Along the western Atlantic coast the American Cow-nosed Ray (distinguished by a divided, fleshy upper lip) occurs spottily from Cape Cod to Brazil. It has a maximum "wingspread" of about 7 feet, and besides being a graceful swimmer, is capable of making prodigious leaps out of the water. The Spotted Eagle Ray of both sides of the tropical Atlantic is an even better jumper.

Lungfishes
ORDER DIPTERIFORMES

As everybody knows, fishes live in water and die in air. With most of the lungfishes it is the other way around; they die if held underwater, and one species has lived for four years out of water in a mud "cocoon."

West African Lungfish

There are six species, one in South America, four in Africa, and one in Australia. Most are 2 to 3½ feet long and are rather eellike in appearance. They live in swamps, small streams, and lakes and feed on worms, insects, crustaceans, frogs, and the like.

The South American and African lungfishes have small, embedded scales and two lungs and look much alike. The Australian Lungfish is very different in both appearance and habits.

Australian Lungfish
DIPTERIFORMES: CERATODONTIDAE

Because of its many differences the Australian Lungfish has been placed in a family of its own. It has large scales and only one lung. Seeking water courses that never dry out, it does not aestivate in mud as the South American and African lungfishes do and in well-aerated water seldom if ever comes to the surface to gulp air. It feeds by pursuing feebly swimming bottom-dwelling fishes or by nibbling aquatic vegetation to get at small animals living in the waterweeds. Because it is strictly protected in Australia, it is seldom exhibited.

South American and African Lungfishes
DIPTERIFORMES: LEPIDOSIRENIDAE

See page 37

The South American Lungfish lives in swamps, streams, and ponds in the equatorial belt of Brazil. Like the African lungfishes, it aestivates, or goes into dry-season sleep, only when the waters of its home dry up; even then its sleeping chamber is quite simple, and it does not surround itself with a mucous cocoon.

See pages 33, 36

The West African Lungfish has been the most thoroughly studied of the group of four African species. When the dry season comes and the waters disappear, it wriggles head downward into the mud for 18 inches or more, forming a cavity for its body and leaving a tunnel to the surface. Until the surface hardens, it rises frequently through the tunnel to gulp air. Eventually it can rise no more, and then, the head pointed upward and the body looped in the middle and doubled back so that the tail covers the eyes, it settles in for the duration. Comparatively enormous mucous glands under the skin secrete an airtight and watertight film around the body and prevent evaporation. Only the mouth is not covered by the film, and in its dry-season sleep the lungfish breathes in and out only about once every two hours. It remains in this position until the returning rains flood the tunnel, soften the mud, and awaken it.

During aestivation the lungfish lives off its muscle tissue, and it has been estimated that it might lose half its weight over a long period. The kidney separates urea from water so that the water can be used over and over again. A concentration of ten to

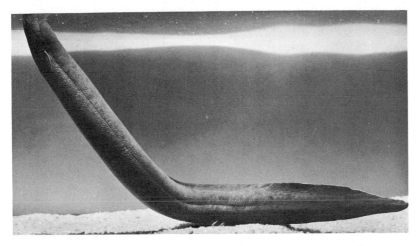

South American Lungfish

West African Lungfish and mud-ball "cocoons" in which similar specimens were shipped from Africa

twenty parts of urea per million would be fatal to most animals, but the lungfish can survive twenty thousand parts per million.

The urea-water ratio returns to about "normal" within twenty-four hours of the lungfish's emergence from the mud. Wrinkled and emaciated, it begins to feed.

West African Lungfish taking a gulp of air

Like the South American Lungfish, the African species dig tunnels in mud for their eggs, of which there are as many as five thousand. The nest is guarded by the male.

ABOVE: *South American Lungfish*
BELOW: *Reedfish*

Bichirs

ORDER POLYPTERIFORMES: POLYPTERIDAE

See page 37

A few living fishes are believed to be derived from very ancient fishes of many millions of years ago, and the bichirs are among these. They and the related Reedfish belong to a small family of eleven species found in rivers and swamps of tropical western Africa and in the Nile.

They have hard scales reminiscent of those of a lizard or snake and a row of five to eighteen flaglike finlets on the back (the generic name means "many fins"); these are most apparent when the fish is swimming slowly. At higher speeds the bichir wriggles and slithers rather like an eel. It has a pair of lungs and can breathe air.

Bichirs are slender and 2 to 3 feet long, and the Congo Bichir is typical.

Congo Bichir

Sturgeons
ORDER ACIPENSERIFORMES: ACIPENSERIDAE

Like the bichirs, the sturgeons have an ancient ancestry. They are probably best known as the source of caviar. Some twenty-one species are found in the Northern Hemisphere, fifteen in central and eastern Europe, and nine in North America; some are landlocked and never enter salt water, others live in the ocean but move into fresh water to spawn.

The Atlantic Sturgeon is one of the latter, spawning in the larger rivers from Maine to Florida; it is the biggest marine fish entering our waters and reaches a length of 10 feet and a weight of 500 pounds. Large as it is, it is dwarfed by the Beluga of the Caspian and Black Seas and the Volga River. The record size for the Beluga is 2,860 pounds and a length of 28 feet. Big sturgeons may produce five million eggs — which is a lot of caviar.

Atlantic Sturgeon

Sturgeons are scaleless except for some bony plates on the body. They are mostly bottom-feeders on snails, worms, insect larvae, and the like, and as they cruise in search of food the fleshy barbels under the snout help detect food, whereupon the low-slung mouth drops down, and the food is sucked in.

A small but odd-looking sturgeon of the Mississippi Valley is the Shovelnose Sturgeon, with a broad and upturned snout. It is seldom more than 3 feet long.

Bowfin
ORDER AMIIFORMES: AMIIDAE

The hardy Bowfin (it can live out of water for as long as twenty-four hours) is the only member of its family and order. Fossils show that it once had a wide distribution in North America, South America, and Europe, but it is now confined to the eastern and central United States.

Bowfin

The Bowfin reaches a maximum size of about 2 feet. A spineless fin runs down the back, and in the males (and sometimes in the females) there is a distinctive large dark spot just forward of the tail.

The female lays her eggs among water plants on the margins of lakes and streams, and the male guards the nest and the young. Bowfins feed on almost any kind of fishes and invertebrates, and their numbers are sometimes controlled if they become too abundant. They are considered trash fish in the North, but are eaten in some parts of the South.

Gars

ORDER LEPISOSTEIFORMES: LEPISOSTEIDAE

When it is stalking its prey—a group of other fishes, perhaps—the Longnose Gar appears to be anything but formidable; it might be merely a drifting stick of wood. Once in position to attack, however, it slashes sideways with its long, teeth-studded snout in a frenzy of action. A fish must be agile indeed to escape such an attack.

Gars are heavily armored with extremely tough scales and have no successful enemies except fishermen, who dislike them because they feed voraciously on other fishes, steal bait, and destroy nets. There are about eight species in fresh waters from southeastern Canada to Costa Rica; some of the Alligator Gars of streams around the Gulf of Mexico get into salt water, however. One Alligator Gar is recorded as being nearly 10 feet long

See page 42

Longnose Gar

Alligator Gar.
WOMETCO MIAMI
SEAQUARIUM PHOTO.

and weighing 302 pounds; the Longnose Gar is considerably smaller. Gars are abundant in the Florida Everglades and are eaten by the Indians of that area.

Tarpons, Herrings, and Their Relatives

ORDER CLUPEIFORMES

This large order contains many well-known fishes—tarpons, bonefishes, herrings, anchovies, salmons, trouts, smelts, and pikes, for example—and also many that are little known except to specialists, such as the weirdly lighted fishes of the great ocean depths. They are grouped together because of certain anatomical characteristics they have in common. Worldwide in distribution, they are found in salt or fresh water, and some enter both.

Tarpons

CLUPEIFORMES: ELOPIDAE

The Tarpon is one of the great game fishes of the world, famed for its spectacular leaps out of the water when hooked. Tarpon fishing is purely a sport—the flesh is seldom eaten—and a time-consuming one; hours may be spent in landing a 200-pound Tarpon. The record catch was 8 feet 3 inches long, with an estimated weight of 340 pounds.

OPPOSITE ABOVE: *Tarpon.* BELOW: *Bonefish*

Tarpons are primarily warm-water fishes and are most often taken in Florida waters and off Tampico, Mexico, but they straggle northward as far as Cape Cod in the summer. Occasionally they enter brackish or fresh water.

Much of our knowledge of the early life of the Tarpon was gained through studies made by the New York Aquarium in a laboratory in Florida in the late 1930's. Hundreds of 7- to 12-inch Tarpons were tagged in evil-smelling pools along the coast around Boca Grande, although these were not considered the major Tarpon nurseries. In their earliest stages Tarpons are ribbonlike and transparent.

A school of young Tarpons in an aquarium tank is always eye-catching as the fishes slowly circle, the light glinting from their large silvery scales. Scales from large Tarpons may be 3 inches across and are sometimes worked into novelties.

Bonefish

CLUPEIFORMES: ALBULIDAE

See page 43

It is debatable whether the Bonefish rivals the Tarpon as a game fish, but it undeniably puts up a good fight against light tackle. Maximum size is 3½ feet and a weight of 18 pounds. There is one shallow-water species, found in warm seas around the world; on the western Atlantic coast it ranges to Cape Cod. The two offshore species are known only to scientists.

The Bonefish is a bottom-feeder. It is not used much for food because of the many small bones. Larval Bonefish are flat, transparent, and bandlike, and large numbers have been seen in West Indian harbors at night.

Herrings

CLUPEIFORMES: CLUPEIDAE

Small as they are—few of the approximately 175 species exceed 18 inches—herrings are among the world's most valuable fishes simply because there are so many of them. The annual catch in the Atlantic and adjacent seas has been estimated at three billion individuals, and vast numbers fall prey to the larger fishes for which herrings are staple food. Out of the thousands of kinds of fishes caught for human consumption, only twenty-nine species are classed as "cardinal," or most important for food, and herrings top the list, with cod and tuna close behind.

Members of the herring family have oily flesh, and some species such as the Atlantic Menhaden are caught for their oil. After the oil is extracted, the residue is used in poultry and cattle feeds.

Menhaden are not a food fish, but the Atlantic Herring is—and an important one on both sides of the Atlantic. A huge fishing industry centers around this species alone.

Herrings have what are called deciduous scales; that is, they are shed easily when the fish is handled or even when it is caught up in a soft net. The enormous shoals of herring feed on minute plankton that enter the mouth as the fish swim, mouth open, and are trapped on a sievelike arrangement of gill rakers attached to the bony arches that support the gill membranes.

The Atlantic Herring produces about thirty thousand eggs (an average). Heavy and adhesive, the eggs sink and are attached to stones and seaweed. Hatching in about twenty-two days at a temperature of 45° F, the young herrings reach maturity in their third year.

Although most herrings live in salt water, some enter brackish or fresh water, and some are confined to fresh water. The Alewife, reaching a maximum of 11 inches, lives not only in the sea from Nova Scotia to Florida but also in inland fresh waters. At one time it created a problem in the Kensico Reservoir north of New York City when its numbers multiplied so greatly that Alewives clogged the screens and bits of fish popped out of city faucets.

Trout and Salmon
CLUPEIFORMES: SALMONIDAE

If there is an aristocracy among fishermen, those who cast for trout and salmon rank high, for these are superb game fishes, as well as fine eating. There are some twenty-odd species in the family, and since their eggs travel well and can be hatched and reared with comparative ease in hatcheries, many have been planted in streams far from their original home.

The Rainbow Trout, for example, was once confined to the Far West, but in the 1880's eggs were propagated by a hatchery in Virginia. Now it is found in streams not only in the Rocky Mountain region but throughout the United States and in Canada, Europe, Hawaii, South Africa, Russia, Japan, New Zealand, India, Australia, Chile, and Argentina. It well deserves such wide distribution, for it is a magnificent fighter when hooked on a fly and puts on a leaping exhibition hardly equaled by any other fish. Where such food as mayflies, caddis flies, larvae of other water insects, and small fishes or mollusks is plentiful, the Rainbow attains a good size rather quickly, and 5- to 8-pounders are not uncommon. The record seems to be a giant 40½ inches long and weighing 37 pounds, taken in Idaho.

The Rainbow does not really have "rainbow" colors; the name comes from the bright red streak along the side that is assumed by the male at spawning time and is lighter in other seasons.

Where it has access to the sea, the Rainbow makes sea runs and is known as a Steelhead.

Another widely introduced trout is the European Brown Trout now living in suitable streams in much of North America. It is handsomely marked with reddish spots on the sides. One weighed in at 39½ pounds.

Trout provide so much good sport that introductions have been made in many places and the graceful little Brook Trout of the Northeastern states and eastern Canada has now been stocked widely, for it thrives in any clear, cold stream. Nowadays it is essentially a hatchery-bred fish, and millions are released annually to be taken by amateur fishermen satisfied with 8- to 10-inch trout. The record was a 31½-inch brookie that weighed 14½ pounds, taken in 1916 in Ontario.

The Atlantic Salmon is essentially a marine species that at spawning time enters rivers on both sides of the Atlantic. In the western Atlantic it ranges from Cape Cod to Hudson Bay.

Spawning takes place far up cold streams, and the eggs are usually deposited in and covered by coarse gravel. The parents then return to the sea, for unlike the Pacific Salmon, they do not

Brown Trout

Brook Trout

necessarily die after spawning. The young go to sea in about two years and return to fresh water to spawn at maturity, often in the fourth year.

Some Atlantic Salmon are landlocked in North America and Europe and never go to sea. The landlocked Sebago Salmon, named after Sebago Lake in Maine, is a well-known sport fish.

Atlantic Salmon have been recorded at a weight of more than 80 pounds. They feed on crustaceans and other fishes.

Pikes

CLUPEIFORMES: ESOCIDAE

One glance at the open mouth of a Northern Pike shows why it has the reputation of being a rapacious feeder on fish, frogs, voles, and water birds. Its mouth is large, with strong and erect teeth on the lower jaw and a fearsome array of small, very sharp, backward-pointing teeth on the roof of the mouth. When a pike gets within striking range of a fish, it makes a swift lunge, seizes its prey sideways, and then swallows it headfirst. There are even records of a hungry pike biting a man. Fish are, however, its usual prey.

The Northern Pike is found in fresh water over most of North America from Ohio northward, except in the Far West, and also in Europe and Asia. It reaches a weight of 46 pounds and a length of 54 inches. Large pikes are often reputed to be very old—some of them hundreds of years old according to European

Northern Pike

Lizardfish
Arawana

Muskellunge

legends—but forty or fifty years is perhaps their maximum longevity.

The Muskellunge of the Great Lakes and nearby areas is the largest member of this family, which contains only five species. The record specimen was 102 pounds in weight.

Bonytongues
CLUPEIFORMES: OSTEOGLOSSIDAE

One of the largest freshwater fishes in the world is in this family: the Arapaima of the Amazon River basin and northern South America. It is sometimes said to reach a length of 15 or even 20 feet, but a conservative 7 or 8 feet is probably more realistic.

The Arapaima is strikingly colored, with large olive green scales on the forward part of its body; near the tail they take on a reddish tint and become bright red at the end. The fish breeds in shallow nests formed in a sandy bottom, and the young—at least in captivity—grow at the rate of 1 to 3 inches a month. Arapaimas are considered good food fish in most of their range.

See page 49
Striking in a different way is the Arawana, of approximately the same range as the Arapaima. It is about 2 feet long, has a mouth that is angled upward so that it looks like the ramp of a combat landing barge and two forked barbels that project from

50

Arapaima

the front edge of the lower jaw. As the Arawana swims, high in the water, the barbels rest at or near the surface; the fish is a surface-feeder, and the barbels may be exploratory organs. It is believed to carry its eggs in its mouth.

The three other species in this family live in Africa and southeastern Asia and Australia.

Lizardfish
ORDER MYCTOPHIFORMES: SYNODONTIDAE

Slender and rather cylindrical, marked with blotches and with a head that reminds one of a reptile, the Lizardfish of the Atlantic coast from Cape Cod to Brazil is well named. It strikes at its prey in a reptilelike way, too; waiting for food, it rests on a sandy bottom with the body angled upward on the pectoral fins. When a small fish swims within range, the Lizardfish lunges and seizes its prey in its sharp teeth. It is about 18 inches long.

See page 49

The Lizardfish is found on both sides of the Atlantic, and there are relatives along the American Atlantic and Pacific coasts and in the Indo-Pacific area. Most are shallow-water fishes.

Gymnarchids

ORDER MORMYRIFORMES: GYMNARCHIDAE

The ability to give off electrical discharges from its tail is one of the peculiarities of an African freshwater fish that for want of a better common name may be called the Nile Gymnarchid. It is unusual, too, in that it has no ventral, anal, or tail fins. However, its dorsal fin is very long and runs almost the entire length of the slender body. The fish reaches a length of about 5 feet. It can move forward or backward with equal ease.

Another peculiarity is its large floating nest, with walls that rise above the water on two sides and one end; the other end, which is the entrance to the nest, is about six inches under the surface of the water. The eggs are exceptionally large, about three-eighths of an inch in diameter.

The electrical discharge of this fish is quite weak and is used not for killing prey but probably for navigation, location of prey, and sex recognition.

Elephant-nose Mormyrid

Mormyrids

MORMYRIFORMES: MORMYRIDAE

Many of the freshwater mormyrids of Africa inevitably remind one of an elephant, for they have a more or less long, downward-curved snout. Indeed, the common name of one species found in the Congo and its tributaries is the Elephant-nose Mormyrid.

The tiny mouth is at the end of the snout in several species. However, the form of the snout and the location of the mouth vary, and in the Ubangi Mormyrid only the lower lip is long— perhaps ½ inch on a 5-inch fish. The mormyrids are mostly bottom-feeders on worms and insect larvae, and the snout is used for probing in mud and between stones. The water in which they live is usually muddy, and mormyrids have poor and often degenerated eyes.

Most of the mormyrids have the ability to give off weak electrical discharges that help them find their way about or communicate with other mormyrids. The discharges create an electrical field, which is distorted by objects that enter it. In turn these distortions are picked up by electroreceptors in the fish's skin.

Blind Cave Fish

Pacu

Bucktoothed Tetra of Guyana and Brazil. (Characidae).

Characins, Minnows, Catfishes, and Their Relatives

ORDER CYPRINIFORMES

Most of the freshwater fishes of the world are in this huge group—some five thousand species as varied as small home-aquarium favorites (Danios, Barbs, Rasboras, Pencilfish, Neon Tetras, etc.), the Electric Eel, North American freshwater catfishes, minnows, carps, suckers, and the Goldfish. They have one thing in common: a chain of small bones called the Weberian ossicles that connect the inner ear with the gasbladder. This apparatus is believed to heighten both the fishes' sensitivity to changes in pressure and their hearing ability. Cypriniforms—the general name for members of this order—can detect sounds of 16 to 17,000 cycles per second, although no one fish can cover this entire range. A Goldfish, for example, can hear frequencies as high as 3,480 cycles per second, a minnow, 7,000 cycles per second.

These fishes are worldwide in distribution; every continent except Australia and Antarctica has enormous numbers of them.

Characins

CYPRINIFORMES: CHARACIDAE

There could hardly be more of a contrast in one family than that between the vicious Piranha and the softly glowing little Neon Tetra; yet they are both characins. But, of course, contrasts are to be expected in a family of about one thousand species occurring from Texas to the lower part of South America and throughout tropical Africa. Another striking difference is size: from a 1-inch tetra to the 125-pound (and dangerous) African Tigerfish.

See page 57

The characins, which might be called the backbone of the typical home aquarium, are diverse in their feeding habits. Some eat only plants, some take plants and insects and other fishes, and some are strictly carnivorous.

To call a Piranha (or Piraya) vicious is not to pass a moral judgment on a fish; the Piranha *is* vicious. Normally it feeds on other fishes in the rivers of tropical South America, but a wounded and bleeding animal will attract a shoal of Piranhas that may reduce it to a skeleton in seconds. There is a record of a 100-pound Capybara that became a mere jumble of bones within a minute after Piranhas attacked it. It is not the size of the Piranha that makes it so feared—the largest of the four species is only about 2 feet long—but the short, sharp teeth in the jutting jaws and the habit of attacking in swarms.

The Neon Tetra is an example of the other extreme among

the scores of characins suitable for home aquariums. The greenish blue stripe along the sides of its 1¼-inch body glows with an almost eerie radiance, and it is easy to see why it has been called "undoubtedly the most popular" of the egg-laying freshwater fishes in home aquariums. It was discovered in 1935 in the headwaters of the Amazon by a butterfly collector who took it secretly to Europe, bred it, and released it astutely to the hobby world; in the early days a single fish sold for as much as $220. Now, of course, it is inexpensive, for it has been imported in vast numbers.

See page 54

The Blind Cave Fish of Mexico is especially interesting, for it was the first blind characin ever found. It was described scientifically in 1936, and four years later the New York Aquarium sent an expedition to La Cueva Chica, a warm-water cave

Gradations in the eyes of the Blind Cave Fish of Mexico. TOP: a blind fish; next, an intermediate with imperfect eyes; then a fully-eyed fish living in the same cave. BOTTOM: a fully-eyed fish from outside waters. All are now considered to be of the same genus.

near the village of Pujal in San Luis Potosí, some 475 miles south of the Mexican border, to study the fish at home. Surprisingly, deep in the cave, one dip of the collecting net brought up little white fishes that were blind, others that had perfect eyes, and still others with intermediate, imperfect eyes. In subsequent years laboratory studies of those fishes became almost a minor industry. The Blind Cave Fish is uniformly white and reaches a length of about 3 inches. Blind though it is, it has an uncanny ability to find food and avoid obstacles.

One of the larger characins is the Pacu of northern South America, which reaches a length of about 27 inches. Oddly enough, while the underside of most fishes is light-colored, the Pacu is greenish gray above, and the sides of the belly are black. It feeds mainly on fruit that falls into its native streams.

See page 54

Skull of Black Piranha, showing the cutting teeth

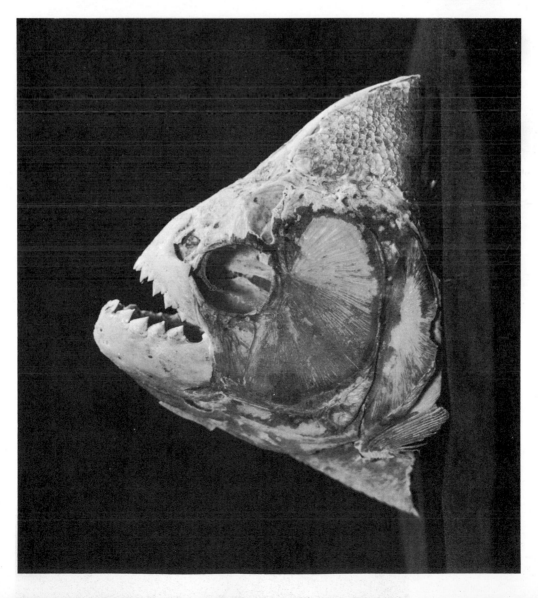

Lustrous Hatchetfish of northern to central South America, a fish that can fly by motions of its fins. (Characidae).

The characins have the distinction of having produced the only fish that actually flies by the motion of its fins. This is the hatchetfish of northern to central South America. The Black-winged Hatchetfish, as an example of several species, has a silvery body with a black horizontal line on top and on the keel of the belly and a black area on its pectoral fins. The fish seems to have an enormously deep abdomen, but this is actually a support for the muscles that move the "wings"—the pectoral fins. Hatchetfish swim and feed near the surface, and when they leap from the water, the pectoral fins move like wings; they can be heard making a buzzing sound. They can fly-glide 10 to 15 feet.

Characins do not have to leave the water to demonstrate their peculiarities. The Tailstander swims with its head up, the

Headstander with its head down. Both live in South American waters. The 4-inch Spotted Headstander of the Guianas usually rests at an angle of 45 degrees and feeds on the bottom with its terminal mouth; some other Headstanders have the mouth on top of the snout and use it to get at small organisms on rocks and plants.

Knifefishes
CYPRINIFORMES: GYMNOTIDAE

The Green Knifefish and the Banded Knifefish are often exhibited and are also well known to home aquarists. As far as is known, all knifefishes have electric organs that generate a weak electrical current used for navigation, communication, and perhaps location of prey.

Both of these knifefishes live in the streams of northern South America, are for the most past nocturnal, and attain a fair size — 18 inches or more.

To see a knifefish is to understand how it gets its name. The body is long and thin, and there are no fins on the top of the body; instead there is a rippling anal fin that may extend four-fifths of the length of the body. There is no tail fin; the knifefish simply tapers off. The long, thin, finless tail is of no use in swimming — the fish moves forward or backward with equal ease by the undulations of its anal fin — but it does serve as a touch organ, and a knifefish that has emerged from a lair among plants or rocks to feed will back in guided by the tip of its tail.

The Green Knifefish has rather iridescent bluish gray stripes on its body and in some lights appears greenish. The Banded Knifefish is more boldly marked with twenty or so white bands around the dark body.

See page 60

Green Knifefish

Mottled Knifefish of eastern Guyana. (Gymnotidae).
Banded Knifefish

Electric Eel
CYPRINIFORMES: ELECTROPHORIDAE

About 250 species of fishes, in many parts of the world and in both fresh and sea water, have the ability to give off electrical discharges. The most powerful of these is the Electric Eel of tropical South America. It is confined to fresh water, reaches a length of 9½ feet (but as usually seen is more likely to be 3 to 6 feet long), and can give off an electrical shock of 650 volts.

A shock of this size—or even the more usual maximum of 350 volts—would certainly be fatal to a man if he happened to be standing in water near an Electric Eel except that the amperage is quite low, about one ampere. Even so, the jolt is more than most people would want to take, and it is sufficient to stun the fishes and frogs on which the Electric Eel feeds.

The dark brown to black Electric Eel moves slowly forward and backward, up and down, by means of its rippling anal fin that runs on the underside of the fish for about four-fifths of its length. The actual body of the fish, the part that contains the digestive and other organs, occupies only the forward one-fifth of the length; the rest of the fish is an electric organ, bundles of specialized tissue that can give off a low pulsating current when the fish is cruising and looking for food and then a high-voltage discharge when food is located or the fish is alarmed. The electrical field created by the low-voltage impulses is distorted by food or other objects in the water, and the change is detected by pits in the eel's head, apparently indicating both the size and nature of the object.

Electric Eels have functional eyes when they are young, but these become cloudy with age. It makes no difference to the eel; it is often found in muddy water where eyes would be of little service, and the low discharge is an efficient food-finder and way-finder.

The only bright color on the Electric Eel is a suffusion of orange on the underside of the head and on the throat. The eel is an air-breather and must come to the surface to gulp air every few minutes.

Electric Eel

Minnows and Carps
CYPRINIFORMES: CYPRINIDAE

"Minnow" is a name that has been applied to many small fishes since the fourteenth century and is still loosely used for almost any small, shining, freshwater fish. Ichthyologists restrict the name to members of this family, but because there are more than 1,500 cyprinid species throughout much of the temperate and tropical world, and some 230 species in North and Central America alone, the chances are pretty good that the layman will be right when he speaks of the minnows he saw in a creek.

Not all cyprinids are "small and shining," however. The Mahseer, a famous game fish of India, may be 9 feet long, and the scales along its lateral line are as large as a man's hand.

The smaller minnows 2 to 4 inches long are not used much for human food, but they are relished by larger and more edible fishes, and fishermen use them as bait. The more brightly colored or curiously marked barbs and rasboras are important to home aquariums, too. Goldfish are cyprinids, although the fancy varieties—Comet, Lionhead, Telescope, Pompom, and many others—have come a long way from the original plain, brownish, wild Goldfish that the Chinese started improving in the tenth century.

See page 64

Two cyprinids of unusual interest are the Stoneroller, which has its long intestine wound around its gasbladder, and the Bitterling, which deposits its eggs in living freshwater mus-

Blind Barb

sels. The Stoneroller lives in streams all over the eastern United States, and at spawning time it carries fine gravel to its nest. The Bitterling is a native of Asia and Europe. It is about 3½ inches long, and in the breeding season the female develops a long tube, called an ovipositor, that she inserts in the gill cavity of a mussel. There her eggs hatch, and eventually the young swim away.

Like the characins, there are blind cave cyprinids—the best-known species being the Blind Barb found only in caves near Thysville, at the mouth of the Congo River in the Republic of the Congo (Belgian Congo). It is a little more than 3 inches long, pinky-white, with fleshy barbels near the mouth. A number of cyprinids have these barbels.

Economically the Carp is perhaps the most important member of the family—where would gefüllte fish be without it?— for it has been planted in many parts of the world, and under   *Carp*

Goldfish

pond cultivation it provides protein at very low cost. Its original home was eastern Europe in the neighborhood of the Black and Caspian seas, but now it is literally found worldwide. In the temperate zone it can grow to 2½ pounds by the end of its third summer, and growth is even more rapid in the tropics. Given time and plenty of food—it is mainly a plant-eater, but will take worms, insects, smaller fishes, and almost anything else—it grows to a maximum of 40 inches and a weight of 60 pounds. Fishermen may dislike it because it pre-empts waters suited to better fish, but as a food resource it is certainly desirable.

Suckers

CYPRINIFORMES: CATOSTOMIDAE

Fishing for suckers with a cane pole and a hook baited with worms or a ball of dough is an old American sport. Suckers are entirely North American fishes, from northern Canada to the Gulf of Mexico, except for one species in China and one in eastern Siberia. Whether Chinese and Siberian boys enjoy the sport is not known, but if they don't, they are missing a lot of fun.

Suckers are bottom-feeders, grubbing for insect larvae, snails, plant material, and the like with the fat-lipped mouth on the underside of the head in most species. Some do not object to muddy water, but most prefer clear, moving water.

The White Sucker is one of the best known of the seventy

White Sucker

or so species and is found in most streams in the eastern and central United States. Occasionally it reaches a weight of 6 pounds, but a good deal less is usual. "Black Sucker" is one of its names, from the fact that the male's back turns very dark at spawning time.

Largest of the suckers is the Bigmouth Buffalo fish of the large rivers of the Mississippi Valley. An 80-pounder was caught in Iowa, but 3 or 4 pounds is about average. This is one sucker in which the mouth is on the end of the head, rather than underneath. It is brownish olive to bluish green above, lighter below.

Smallmouth Buffalo

The Smallmouth Buffalo of the Mississippi drainage does not reach the maximum size of the Bigmouth.

Buffalo fish are sometimes found in prodigious numbers. Five thousand pounds of Buffalo fish were removed from a 135-acre lake in Missouri when it was drained, and many weighed 20 to 30 pounds.

Loaches
CYPRINIFORMES: COBITIDAE

A reputation for being able to forecast a storm is one of the distinctions of certain loaches, a family of small, elongated freshwater fishes of the Old World. Whether the reputation is deserved is another matter—a good deal of imagination seems to enter into descriptions of greatly increased activity by the Spotted Weatherfish and the European Weatherfish twenty-four hours before a storm.

Loaches have a number of barbels around the mouth—fleshy appendages like those of a catfish—and in some there is a movable spine under or in front of each eye. What purpose it serves is not known.

The method of respiration is curious: the fish rises to the surface, takes a gulp of air, and as the air passes through the intestine, oxygen is absorbed.

Several loaches are excellent home-aquarium fishes, and the Clown Loach of Sumatra, Borneo, and the Sunda Islands is quite as colorful as some of the coral reef fishes. Its body is almost orange, and three broad, velvety-black bands encircle it.

The fins are bright red. It is seldom more than 3 or 4 inches long, is hardy, and has lived for twenty-five years in an aquarium. The sexes are marked alike and cannot be distinguished except by dissection.

Clown Loach (left) and Black Ruby Barb of Ceylon. (Cyprinidae).

The Spotted Weatherfish has an enormous range, from western Europe to China, in a number of subspecies. While it is not as spectacular as the Clown Loach, its yellowish brown, 4-inch body is prettily marked with rows of spots. It scatters its eggs indiscriminately on sand, among plant stems, or even over a muddy bottom.

Sea Catfishes
CYPRINIFORMES: ARIIDAE

Many fishes are casual about their eggs and young, others are more solicitous, but few more so than the sea catfishes. Males carry the eggs in their mouths and give the same shelter to the young after they hatch.

About forty species of sea catfish are known to practice this oral brooding. They are found around the world in temperate and tropical waters, some species in the sea and some in brackish water. Typically catfishlike, they have a scaleless body and fleshy barbels around the mouth. They differ from freshwater catfishes in keeping on the move, rather than resting on the bottom, and in traveling in schools.

The American Sea Catfish is found along the Atlantic coast from Cape Cod to Panama. Its eggs are very large—although not as large as those produced by some other species of sea catfishes, which may be nearly an inch in diameter—and a sizable male has been known to carry as many as fifty-five in his mouth. He holds them there for a month and then shelters the young for another two weeks to a month, fasting all the while.

The Gafftopsail Catfish is another Atlantic coast species of about the same range and with the same incubating habits.

Sea Catfish

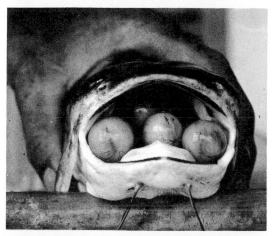

Gafftopsail Catfish with mouth forced open to show eggs being brooded. E. W. GUDGER PHOTO.

Tourists in the West Indies and northern South America often bring back cleaned skulls of sea catfishes, said to come from the "Crucifix Fish." The underside of the skull does bear a strong resemblance to a man with arms outstretched on a cross; there is even a halo!

Marine Catfishes
CYPRINIFORMES: PLOTOSIDAE

See page 72

As everybody knows who has handled a catfish carelessly, it has sharp spines that can inflict a painful wound. The Marine Catfish of the Indo-Pacific coasts and estuaries goes a good deal further; its three spines bear venom glands that can cause death.

The Marine Catfish is usually 10 to 12 inches long—at least one species reaches 30 inches—and travels in schools along the shore. Young ones have stripes the length of the body, one above and one below the tail.

North American Freshwater Catfishes
CYPRINIFORMES: ICTALURIDAE

A well-known Florida professor, writing a key to fishes, is said to have dismissed the catfishes with one line: "Any damn fool knows a catfish."

It is true that the freshwater catfishes of North America all have that catfish look: "whiskers" around the broad mouth, smooth skin, mostly plain dark above and whitish or yellowish below. But they do have some differences in coloration and in size—from the 2- to 3½-inch Tadpole Madtom to the 5½-foot Flathead.

There are nearly thirty species in this family of catfish, and one kind or another is found from Canada to Guatemala, in rivers and mud-bottomed creeks, in ponds and lakes, and even in clear cold streams quite suitable for trout. In general they are bottom feeders and will eat anything—worms, insect larvae, fish eggs, small fishes, plant material, dead animal flesh. Scavengers though they are in some of their feeding habits, they are excellent eating, and gourmets who are disdainful of their alleged "muddy taste" have surely never experienced a well-fried 6-inch

Flathead Catfish

Brown Bullheads in spawning posture

Blue, or Mississippi, Catfish

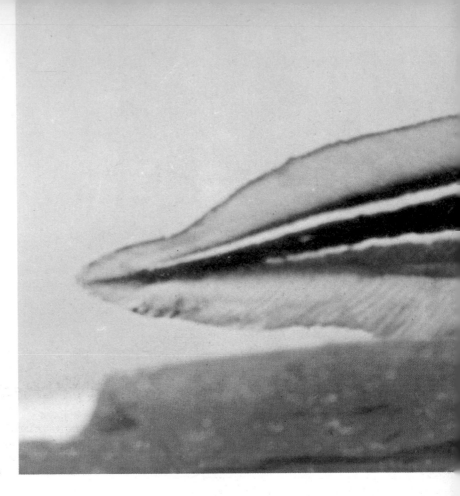

Marine Catfish

"fiddler cat" from the rivers of Tennessee. "Catfish farms" are a thriving industry in some southern and midwestern states.

These freshwater catfishes seek out protected sites, such as the cavity under a rock ledge, the interior of a sunken hollow log, or even underwater muskrat burrows for their eggs. The bullheads, originally of the eastern United States but now introduced in the West, in Hawaii, and in Europe, guard their eggs and keep them aerated by swimming around them. The young cats form a dense school after hatching and for a while are guarded by the See page 71 male. Most Brown Bullheads are taken at a length of about a foot, but the related Black Bullhead and Yellow Bullhead are sometimes quite large; a 24-inch, 8-pound Black Bullhead was taken in Lake Waccabuc, New York.

For real size, however, honors go to the Blue, or Missis- See page 71 sippi, Catfish, with a 150-pounder on record, and the celebrated Channel Catfish that is fished commercially—one weighing 57 pounds was pulled out of the Santee-Cooper Reservoir in South Carolina. The average, though, is more likely to be 1 or 2 pounds.

The venom-spined little Tadpole Madtom of the north-

Brown Bullhead

eastern United States and down the Atlantic coast is likely to be found in mud-bottomed lakes and small, still streams.

Clariid Catfishes
CYPRINIFORMES: CLARIIDAE

Throughout Africa and across southern Asia to the Philippines are some curious catfishes with accessory air-breathing organs connected with the gill chamber. They can live in very stagnant water and often come out on shore at night in search of food or a new home—hence a common name of "Walking Catfishes." Several species are imported for the home-aquarium trade.

A broad mouth in a flattened head and four pairs of barbels around the mouth mark the West African Eel Catfish as a catfish, but there is more eel than catfish in the rest of the foot-long, slim body. There are two species. The more slender of the two is the Eel Catfish of the Congo and Angola, which is a uniform dark brown; the West African species has greenish, violet, or rusty areas on its body.

See page 76
The Albino Clarias of southern Asia is imported for the hobbyists; it is an attractive, pinky-white catfish, complete with barbels and up to 18 inches long. The albino form is apparently established in nature. The normal coloration is brownish to green-blue, with pale spots on the flanks. The accidental introduction of these fishes in Florida has caused havoc among native game fishes, for the "Walking Catfishes" can travel overland and spread rapidly, and compete with native fishes for food and space.

Upside-down Catfishes
CYPRINIFORMES: MOCHOKIDAE

Most fishes swim upside-down only when they are sick, injured, or dying. The Upside-down Catfish of tropical Africa usually swims that way—not always, but a good part of the time.

There are about thirty-six species of these little fishes, all from warm fresh water, and at least six species swim on their backs.

The mouth is on the underside of the head, and when the fish swims at the surface, it can readily take floating food; on the bottom it feeds right side up, and its barbels seem to come into play to help it find food.

Specimens of the Congo Upside-down Catfish have grown from 1¼ inches to 6 inches in five years in the New York Aquarium. Merely dark brownish at first, they became covered with scrawl markings as they grew older.

Unmistakable representations of Upside-down Catfish have been noticed carved on ancient Egyptian monuments.

Congo Upside-down Catfish

Albino Clarias, or "Walking Catfish"

Electric Catfish
CYPRINIFORMES: MALAPTERURIDAE

See page 78

The Electric Catfish of tropical Africa and the Nile Valley grows to a length of 4 feet and a weight of 50 pounds and can give off a discharge of about 350 volts — not as much as the South American Electric Eel, but a considerable jolt nevertheless. It is the only catfish with electrical powers.

Small Electric Catfishes are sometimes kept in home aquariums. The pinkish body has some black spots, two dark bars just forward of the tail with creamy color between, and a tail fin tipped with black.

The Electric Catfish does not send out a continuous "locating" series of electrical impulses, but fires its battery in one big jolt and follows it with milder shocks.

This is another fish well known to the ancient Egyptians; it is depicted on tombs.

Eels
ORDER ANGUILLIFORMES

Most of the approximately 350 species of eel in this order live in temperate or tropical seas around the world. Some sixteen species do inhabit fresh water, but they go to the sea to spawn and die. All are snakelike in form, most lack scales, though a few have them embedded in the skin, and their fins are usually confined to the dorsal and anal, which usually join up with the tail fin; a few have pectoral fins. They swim with a serpentine motion.

The early life of many of the eels is perhaps the most interesting and unusual thing about them. At hatching the young eel is called a leptocephalus, and it is ribbonlike and transparent. The curious story of the transformation of the leptocephalus into an elver (or glass eel) on its way to adulthood will be discussed in the account of the European and American Eels.

Freshwater Eels
ANGUILLIFORMES: ANGUILLIDAE

From the time of the ancient Greeks until the early years of this century, the life history of the freshwater eel was a fascinating mystery to naturalists. One old theory was that they were produced by the dew on a May morning; another, that they were the offspring of "a small beetle." But around 1906 a Danish biologist, Professor Johannes Schmidt, worked it out: eels on both sides of the Atlantic and around the Mediterranean leave their homes in freshwater streams and ponds, make their way to the Sargasso Sea south of Bermuda, and there they spawn — and

TOP: *Electric Catfish*
CENTER:
American Eel
RIGHT:
Spotted Moray

die. Eventually their offspring work their way back to the areas from which their parents came.

The European Eel and the American Eel have different numbers of vertebrae and are considered different species. In the late 1950's, however, an alternative to the Schmidt explanation was offered—that there is really only one species, that European Eels are simply the offspring of American Eels, and that the young become "American" or "European" depending on the current that catches them. Schmidt's classic account is still widely accepted, however.

Like its American relative, the European Eel lives in freshwater ponds, creeks, rivers, and lakes. Females are about twelve years old and perhaps 5 feet long when the urge to spawn strikes them; males start for the sea when they are four to eight years old and less than 2 feet long. At this time their normal yellow color changes to silver, and they are fat—and very good eating. They may have to travel three or even four thousand miles to reach the spawning grounds.

The ribbonlike leptocephali hatch from floating eggs and feed at a depth of 60 to 150 feet, gradually drifting and wriggling eastward toward Europe, taking about three years to reach the coasts. Here they change into elvers, or glass eels, shrinking from about 3 inches to 2½ inches, and begin their ascent up streams, even overland on dewy nights if there is no other way to get back to the places from which their parents came.

The story is much the same for the American Eel except that it does not have so far to go—perhaps one thousand miles—and makes the journey in about one year.

Eels are omnivorous feeders and even scavengers. On their spawning migrations, however, they do not feed.

Morays
ANGUILLIFORMES: MURAENIDAE

Morays belong to the same zoological order as the freshwater European and American Eels, but in disposition they certainly have nothing in common; the reef-dwelling morays have a well-earned reputation for ferocity when provoked.

Morays of some eighty species are inhabitants of coral reefs in warm seas in many parts of the world. The Green Moray, common from the Florida Keys to Rio de Janeiro, is usually bright green, but may be brownish, slaty gray, or occasionally mottled. Its thick and leathery skin has a mucous coating responsible in part for its color; scraped off, the slime is yellow, and the skin beneath is bluish slate in color, the combination giving the green appearance.

See page 80

Morays usually lurk in crevices in coral reefs or among

Green Morays

rocks, with the head and a few inches of the body protruding and the well-armed mouth slowly opening and closing. This action makes them appear more aggressive than they really are, for the movements of the mouth are actually for the purpose of pumping water across the gills. Morays ordinarily hide by day and forage for crustaceans and small fish by night.

In some parts of the world morays are considered good eating, and the Green Moray is often seen in the market in Bermuda. The Spotted Moray, reaching a length of about 3 feet, is probably the commonest West Indian moray.

See page 78

Conger Eels
ANGUILLIFORMES: CONGRIDAE

Conger Eels look very much like freshwater eels, but they are entirely marine and are found almost around the world in warm and temperate seas. From shallow water they move to deeper water at spawning time and subsequently die. The larvae are thin and transparent ribbons—again much like those of the freshwater eels.

Congers occasionally reach a length of 8 feet and a weight of 12 pounds, but most are under 4 feet long. They feed on small fish and marine worms.

Needlefishes
ORDER BELONIFORMES: BELONIDAE

Needlefishes are probably so called because they are long and slender of body and their jaws are almost grotesquely elongated, but the name would be equally appropriate because of the armament of fine and needle-sharp teeth within those jaws.

Atlantic Needlefish

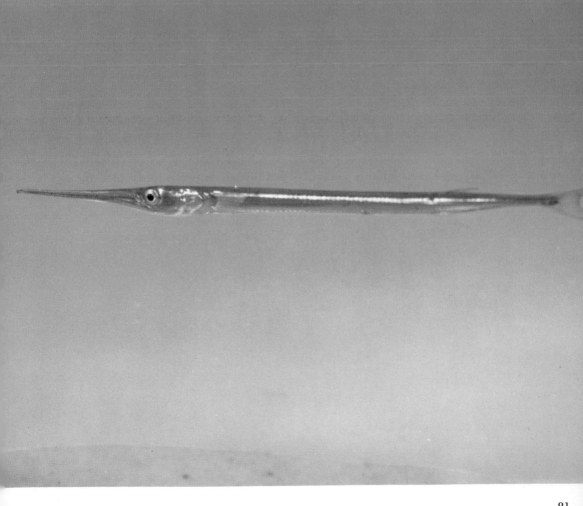

There are some sixty species in tropical and temperate seas. The Atlantic Needlefish (also called Billfish or Silver Gar) is found along the Atlantic and Gulf coasts, but is not common north of Cape Cod. It sometimes ascends rivers. Typically it swims near the surface and often thrusts its thin jaws out of the water. It feeds on small fishes.

Needlefish eggs have tufts of long threads that catch on objects in the water, so that masses of eggs are anchored. The fish may reach a length of about 4 feet, but that size is rare.

Flyingfish in flight. The fish do not flap the fins; they only glide. H. E. EDGERTON PHOTO.

Flyingfishes
BELONIFORMES: EXOCOETIDAE

Most fishes can be better seen and appreciated in an aquarium tank than at liberty in open water. The Atlantic Flyingfish can, of course, be closely studied in a small tank, but appreciation of its specialty—soaring—requires a tank that would, preferably, be several hundred feet long.

It used to be thought that flyingfishes vibrated their "wings" much like an insect, but high-speed photography shows that the greatly enlarged pectoral fins and the large pelvic fins are held steady; the motive power for the flight comes from vigorous beating of the tail with its long lower lobe, and once the fish leaves the water, it simply soars on its outstretched "wings." Air currents may catch it and lift it high—as much as 20 feet onto the deck of a ship, for example.

The Atlantic Flyingfish reaches a length of about 15 inches. It is dark blue above, silvery on the sides and below, and the pectoral fins are transparent, as are the tips of the pelvic fins. Its range is from about Maine eastward to England and southward to Brazil, and it is most often seen, from ships, over deep water.

Codfishes
ORDER GADIFORMES: GADIDAE

It has been estimated that 400 million codfish are taken each year in the North Atlantic and adjacent seas. The Atlantic Cod is, indeed, one of the most valuable food fishes in the world, and salted cod has been a never-failing food resource for centuries. *See page 85*

The Atlantic Cod is speckled on the sides, has three dorsal and two anal fins and a small barbel under the chin. It is a bottom-feeding fish at depths of 1,500 feet or more, and nowadays most of the catch is taken by trawling nets that sweep up shoals of fish near the bottom. Fishes of every size are thus taken, perhaps most in the range of 2½ to 25 pounds, but a cod 6 feet long and weighing 211 pounds is on record.

The egg productivity of the cod is fantastic—some nine million eggs from a 75-pound fish. Fortunately mortality is equally high, or else all the cold oceans would not have room for the codfish. Other fish eat the eggs, and many are killed by changes in water temperature and other natural hazards. For a time the eggs float, and after hatching the larval fishes themselves float for two months or more, and of course, many fall prey to other fishes during this time. Those that survive sink to the bottom when they are about 1 inch long, feed and grow there, and in five years are ready to add their own millions of eggs to the ocean nursery.

The Atlantic Cod is not the only valuable member of the family. Shore dwellers from Labrador to Virginia know the Atlantic Tomcod as the Frostfish and scoop up the foot-long fishes when they spawn close inshore from November to February. Other good food fishes include the Pollock, which averages about 4 pounds and occurs on both sides of the Atlantic—on the western side to Cape Cod and occasionally a little farther south; the 18-inch Spotted Hake of Cape Cod to North Carolina; the White Hake, up to 3½ feet in length and a weight of 30 pounds, found from Newfoundland to Cape Hatteras in rather deep waters; and the Haddock, well known on the breakfast table as finnan haddie. It is caught on both sides of the North Atlantic, on this side as far south as New Jersey and in deeper waters off Cape Hatteras. In recent years overfishing has caused concern. The Haddock reaches quite a good size; the maximum is a length of 44 inches and a weight of 36 pounds.

Finnan haddie, incidentally, gets its name from the town of Findon in Scotland where the salting and smoking of the fish was developed in the middle of the eighteenth century.

Hake has come into prominence as the source of the fish protein concentrate (FPC) known as "fish flour," in which the whole fish is ground up, emulsified, and dried, and used as an odorless ingredient of bread, macaroni, cookies, and the like. It is becoming especially important in countries that are poor in protein resources.

A familiar member of the family is the Squirrel Hake of the Gulf of St. Lawrence to Virginia, also called the Ling. Its young are said to seek shelter in the mantle cavity of large ocean scallops. It may be 27 inches long and weigh 8 pounds.

Tomcod
OPPOSITE: *Squirrel Hake*

Atlantic Cod
Spotted Hake

Sticklebacks, Seahorses, and Their Relatives

ORDER GASTEROSTEIFORMES

Some fishes that are superficially quite unlike — such as the sticklebacks and the seahorses — have been combined in this zoological order because of certain anatomical characteristics. In some systems of classification sticklebacks are placed in one order (Thoracostei), and trumpetfish, shrimpfish, seahorses, and pipefish in another (Solenichthyes).

Sticklebacks
GASTEROSTEIFORMES: GASTEROSTEIDAE

Some Sticklebacks are as much at home in fresh water as in the sea, they have especially interesting nesting habits, and they do well in home aquariums.

See page 88

The Threespine Stickleback is a 4-inch fish that occurs around the world in northern salt and fresh water and gets as far south as New Jersey along our coast and to Spain and Italy (where it is primarily a freshwater fish) in Europe.

Stickleback nests vary somewhat according to species, but it is always the male that builds the nest. With the onset of the spawning season in spring or early summer, the Threespine Stickleback takes on a brilliant red color below, and his natural pugnacity is increased as he battles other males. He selects the nest site, which may be around the stems of water plants, and gathers algae and bits of plant material that he holds in place by means of sticky threads secreted from the kidney. When he is satisfied with the nest — and sometimes he may have several of them — he corrals a ripe female by nipping at her fins and driving her until she enters the nest and deposits her eggs. She then leaves, and the male enters and fertilizes the eggs with milt. He guards the eggs, swimming around the nest and creating a current with his fins or, as in the Fourspine Stickleback, sucking water through it from a hole on top. After the eggs hatch, in a week or a little longer, the male guards the young, and if one strays, he takes it in his mouth and spits it back into the nest.

Two of the sticklebacks along the American coast are the Fourspine from New Brunswick and Nova Scotia to Virginia, 1½ to 2½ inches long, and the Ninespine Stickleback, about 3 inches long, that gets south to the New Jersey area.

Trumpetfish
GASTEROSTEIFORMES: AULOSTOMIDAE

The 2-foot Trumpetfish that ranges from the West Indies to southern Florida is a bizarre denizen of the coral reefs. It is

OPPOSITE: *Male Fourspine Stickleback weaving a nest*

*Threespine
Stickleback*

Trumpetfish.
WOMETCO MIAMI
SEAQUARIUM PHOTO.

88

slender, stiff-bodied from the bony plates in the skin, and its head and snout are very long; the mouth is at the end of the snout. A Trumpetfish has been seen to insert its snout into a coral head and suck a damselfish out of its lair.

Skin divers have described it as swimming head downward. This posture is a camouflage device that helps to conceal it among sea whips and other "stalky" invertebrates.

Despite its small mouth, the Trumpetfish can swallow surprisingly large prey—one that was 22½ inches long contained a Demoiselle about 2¾ inches long and more than an inch in body depth.

Shrimpfish
GASTEROSTEIFORMES: CENTRISCIDAE

A Shrimpfish is not related to the shrimps, but if one is held *See page 90* in the hand, it is easy to see how it acquired the name. Its body is encased in a thin, bony, transparent covering of plates, reminiscent of the exoskeleton of shrimps. This is not the only oddity of the Shrimpfish, however. How it swims, head up or head down, has been debated since the early years of this century.

There are only four species of Shrimpfish, all in the warm seas from East Africa to Australia and Hawaii; they are not found in the Atlantic. The body is long and thin, the snout very long, and a dark stripe runs along the sides and to the end of the snout. Most of the fins are crowded together at the rear of the body.

Despite all the debate, it is now known that the Shrimpfish *can* swim either head down or head up, as well as horizontally. The head-down position is commonest. As it swims, it rises and falls, and several swimming together may turn in unison on their long axis, now with the belly forward, now with the back. Their movements are leisurely as they forage for minute bits of food, but if frightened, they shoot away in a horizontal position.

In the Aquarium, Shrimpfish must be fed newly hatched brine shrimp daily.

Seahorses and Pipefishes
GASTEROSTEIFORMES: SYNGNATHIDAE

The upright-swimming, horse-headed, prehensile-tailed seahorses and the slender pipefishes—some so thin there hardly seems room for the necessary internal organs—are close relatives despite their dissimilarity of appearance. Each is encased in body armor, as well as having an internal skeleton, and the tiny mouth is at the end of a long snout. They are alike, too, in their reproductive behavior. The female deposits her eggs in or on the body of the male, and he broods them.

Seahorses are found in temperate and warm, mostly coastal waters in many parts of the world and range from the 1½-inch

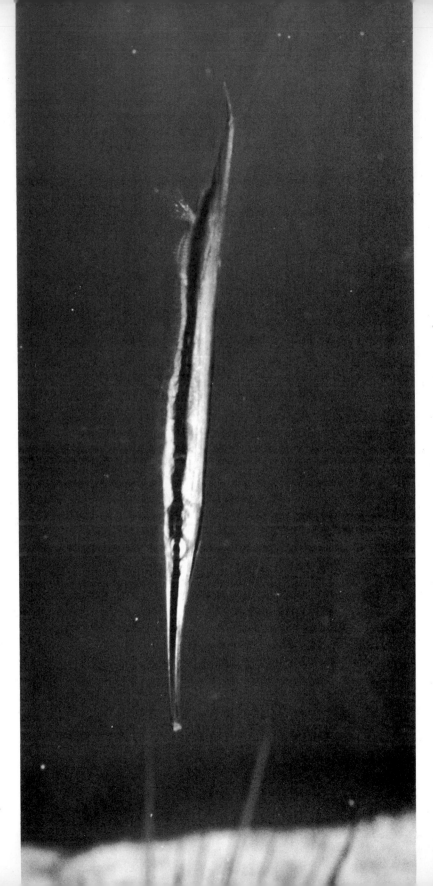

Shrimpfish

Two color phases of the Spotted Seahorse

BELOW LEFT: *Northern Pipefish*
BELOW: *Banded Pipefish of the Indo-Pacific. (Syngnathidae).*

See page 91

Dwarf Seahorse of the Gulf of Mexico to comparative giants measuring 12 inches from the top of the head to the tip of the forward-curling tail. Along the American coast the Spotted Seahorse is abundant — in some years — from Nova Scotia to Argentina. It has three color phases, red, creamy, and dark, almost black, and reaches a length of about 7 inches.

At spawning time the female employs her ovipositor, an organ by which she places her eggs in a pouch under the tail of the male. After about six weeks the one hundred or more perfectly formed young are expelled from the pouch by convulsive movements of the male's body. The little seahorses, about five-eighths of an inch long, swim away and begin feeding on live food. Minute brine shrimp are provided for them in the Aquarium, and they suck these up through their tubular mouths too fast for the eye to follow.

Seahorses are maintained easily enough in a saltwater aquarium — even the birth of the babies has been photographed in the New York Aquarium — but they are difficult to keep in a home aquarium. The Dwarf Seahorse is reasonably hardy, however.

See page 91

Breeding behavior in the pipefishes is much like that of the seahorses except that in some the eggs are placed on the underside of the abdomen or under the tail and may or may not be enclosed in a fold of skin, depending on the species. The Northern Pipefish, occasionally reaching a length of 12 inches, ranges from Halifax to North Carolina and is abundant in the New York area, usually in seaweed in shallow water. It spawns in the late spring and early summer.

Killifishes and Their Relatives
ORDER CYPRINODONTIFORMES

Many popular home-aquarium fishes belong to this order, which includes killifishes, four-eyed fishes, livebearers, and cavefishes. Most inhabit fresh water and have a New World distribution, although some of the egg-layers in the killifish group are found from southern Europe into Africa and the Far East.

Killifishes
CYPRINODONTIFORMES: CYPRINODONTIDAE

Hardiness is a characteristic of the little killifishes that abound along our Atlantic coast. The Common Killifish, or Mummichog, may be found in small or large schools in bays and marshes, often in water unfit for almost any other fish. Among the many good things that can be said for them are that they make excellent bait for fishermen, that they devour millions of mosquito larvae, and that any home aquarist can easily collect

Striped Killifish
Common Killifish, or Mummichog

all he wants for his tanks. Furthermore, marine biologists use them for many kinds of research.

The Common Killifish ranges all the way from the Gulf of St. Lawrence to the Gulf of Mexico. During the spawning season in the spring the males assume brilliant colors with orange and bluish reflections. Young Killifish are well developed when they hatch from the amber-colored eggs. Adults reach a length of 5 inches.

See page 93

Largest of the northern killifishes is the Striped Killifish, sometimes 8 inches long. The sexes are marked differently: the male has short vertical bars on the sides, while the female usually has three or four longitudinal dark lines. Eggs are somewhat larger than those of the Common Killifish, but are also amber and are usually buried in the sand.

One of the prettiest of the killies is the Sheepshead Minnow of Cape Cod to Texas, which is rather stout of body. The male takes on a brilliant steel blue above and orange below in the breeding season. These killies have been found alive in Texas shore ponds where the water was four times as salty as sea water.

Usually found in brackish water, although it is not uncommon in fresh water, is the little 2-inch Rainwaterfish. It ranges from Connecticut to Key West, and in the southern part of its range it lives in sea water.

Four-eyed Fish
CYPRINODONTIFORMES: ANABLEPIDAE

While it is not strictly accurate to say that the Four-eyed Fish has four eyes, it is true that the two actual eyes are divided into upper and lower halves for vision above and below the water, and each half has its own specially adapted part of the retina.

The Four-eyed Fish inhabits fresh and brackish waters from southern Mexico to northern South America. It is usually 6 to 8 inches long, occasionally 12 inches.

Typically it floats just under the surface of the water with the "air" half of its eyes protruding. It is not known to use its air eyes for sighting insects or other prey; the presumption is that it keeps a lookout for predators. When frightened, it can make vigorous leaps out of the water.

The one to five young are born alive.

Livebearers
CYPRINODONTIFORMES: POECILIIDAE

Guppies, platys, swordtails, mollies—through these representatives even the beginning home aquarist is likely to have an acquaintance with this large family of livebearing topminnows.

It is a widespread family, inhabiting fresh and salt water from below the Great Lakes to Argentina. *Four-eyed Fish*

Internal fertilization of the female by the male is the rule in the family, and this is effected by an organ, called a gonopodium, formed by the forward rays of the male's anal fin. These elongated rays readily identify the male; the female's anal fin is evenly rounded.

Guppies are among the most popular of hobby fishes, and an astonishing number of variants from the wild type have been produced. The wild Guppy is certainly not strikingly handsome —a little gray fish with bright-colored spots, so common in the streams of Trinidad and nearby northern South America that one of its familiar names in Trinidad is "Millions." A British inspector of schools in Trinidad scooped up a few "Millions" one day in the middle of the last century and sent them to the British Museum, where they were eventually named *Girardinus guppyi*

Green Swordtails, female above and male below

in honor of the collector, Robert John Lechmere Guppy. Later it was discovered that a man named Peters had sent the same fish sometime earlier, and it had been given a different name — which, being earlier, was the official one. However, "Guppy" must have sounded like a good name for a hobby fish, for that was the name that stuck when it was introduced into the home-aquarium trade in 1908.

Platy and swordtail are the common names of two closely related fishes in pools, ponds, and clear streams from southern Mexico to Guatemala. Both have been bred to a variety of colors and are popular with hobbyists because they are so easy to breed and keep. The male swordtail is distinguished by a very long extension of the caudal fin—in the wild swordtail it may even be longer than the body.

Wild Platyfish as it appears in nature

Platys and swordtails have become important in medical research, especially in the genetics of cancer, for black cancerous growths can be induced by crossing the Spotted Platy with the Green Swordtail.

See page 96

Mollies (the name comes from the generic name, *Mollienesia*) are popular with aquarists because of the huge dorsal fin of the male. The Sailfin Mollie lives in brackish to fresh water from the southeastern United States to Yucatan. Like most home-aquarium fishes, it has been bred to a variety of colors.

An extraordinary thing about the Amazon Mollie of southern Texas and northeastern Mexico is that it produces only female offspring. Its reproductive processes are stimulated by males of related species found in the same waters, but the young are not hybrids and are carbon copies of their mother. This fish is called a "sexual parasite."

Perhaps the most valuable member of the family is one that is not a hobby fish at all; it is the tiny Mosquitofish of the southern United States from Alabama to eastern Texas. It is celebrated for being able to eat its own weight in mosquito larvae day after day, and as a result, has been shipped to many warm parts of the world to help keep down mosquitoes. It does not require especially warm conditions; some strains of the Mosquitofish tolerate water so cold it is almost freezing — and also water at 85° F. Males are about 1¼ inches long, females 2¼ inches. They are not particularly pretty, the back is brown and the sides are gray with a bluish shimmer, and in a community tank they are aggressive toward other fish. But they do devour mosquitoes!

Cavefishes
CYPRINODONTIFORMES: AMBLYOPSIDAE

The limestone regions of the central United States have five species of fish that live in caves or spring systems; with one other species in swamps and streams from Virginia to central Georgia they make up this small family. There are cave-dwelling fishes in other parts of the world, but they belong to different families.

Blindness is, of course, no handicap to fishes that live in the perpetual darkness of underground streams, and the Southern Cavefish, the Northern Cavefish, the Ozark Cavefish, and a fourth newly discovered and as yet unnamed species (*Typhlichthys* sp.) are quite blind, with merely rudimentary eyes. The Spring Cavefish that is found in spring systems instead of caves proper does have poorly developed eyes that are at least partly functional, but it can find its food perfectly well if they are removed experimentally. To compensate for the loss of vision, the cavefishes have sensory organs in ridges on the head, body, and tail that probably serve the same purpose as the lateral line in

Golden Black Wagtail Platy, a hybrid

other fishes and enable them to detect movements in the water around them.

The Northern Cavefish is the famous blind fish of Mammoth Cave in Kentucky and also of other limestone caves in Indiana and Tennessee. It was first described in 1842. It is white, 1 to 6 inches long, and produces its young from eggs that are carried in the gill chamber of the female. This is also believed to be the practice with other members of the family.

The Swampfish of the Atlantic coastal plain lives in the open and has functional eyes. It has some color—a dark streak along the sides.

Squirrelfish
ORDER BERYCIFORMES: HOLOCENTRIDAE

Squirrelfish of the tropical Indo-Pacific. (Holocentridae).

Explore a coral reef in almost any tropical sea and you are likely to come across one of the seventy or so species of squirrelfish, resting quietly in a crevice or under a coral overhang by day

and foraging by night. It will probably be bright red, either plain or streaked or spotted with white, and it will stare at you with almost grotesquely squirrellike eyes. Indeed, one of the squirrel-fishes of the tropical Indo-Pacific is called the Wistful Squirrel-fish from its pathetic look. The large eyes are an adaptation to the nocturnal habits of squirrelfish.

The Squirrelfish of shallow-water reefs from Florida to Brazil is usually about 1 foot long, sometimes 2 feet. It is a market fish in the West Indies, but has little food value.

Squirrelfish are sometimes called Soldierfish after their armament of sharp spines on the gill covers and fins.

Snakeheads
ORDER CHANNIFORMES: CHANNIDAE

Indian jugglers sometimes exhibit Snakeheads out of water, demonstrating how they wriggle and "swim" on dry land for hours with no apparent discomfort. The secret is, of course, that

Snakehead

they are air-breathers. They cannot exist indefinitely out of water, but they can stay alive for at least a day. When they move from pond to pond in search of other fishes for food, they "swim" ahead on the ground with about the same motions they use in water.

Snakeheads are found in Africa and Asia. They are 6 inches to 3 feet long and are rather cylindrical in body form, with a somewhat flattened head reminiscent of a snake's. Most are strongly barred or blotched on the sides and back. They are an excellent food fish and are cultivated in ponds in some places, but are so voracious that they soon eliminate other good fishes.

Perchlike Fishes
ORDER PERCIFORMES

This enormous zoological order includes perhaps eight thousand species of fish, both marine and freshwater, of a diversity too great for generalizations to be drawn. They are worldwide in distribution, and among them are valuable food fishes, as well as some of the most decorative little fishes of any waters.

Snooks
PERCIFORMES: CENTROPOMIDAE

The sport fisherman who has landed a 30-pound Snook in the Florida Keys may not always realize it, but the 2-inch Glassfish in his home aquarium is a very close relative of the Snook. So, for that matter, is the 200-pound Nile Perch. The family is a small one, but certainly varied.

The Snook's name comes from the Dutch *snoek*, meaning pike; the fish is also called a Robalo, the Spanish word for bass. It attains a length of 4 feet, occasionally more—one 56 inches long and weighing 50½ pounds is on record—and is both an active game fish and very good eating, with white and flaky flesh. It ranges through the Gulf of Mexico and the West Indies, usually associated with mangroves, and is also found on the other side of the tropical Atlantic and in the tropical eastern Pacific. It sometimes runs into fresh waters.

Glassfish are so abundant in rice paddies and other shallow fresh waters in northern India that they are used as fertilizer. They are well named, for the skeleton and internal organs can be seen through the transparent body.

Sea Basses and Groupers
PERCIFORMES: SERRANIDAE

Millions of pounds of these fishes are harvested from the tropical and temperate seas every year, but apart from their value as food, they have another claim on the aquarium visitor's inter-

Filamentous Glassfish

est—some of them have the ability to change color almost instantaneously.

Eight radical color changes in the Nassau Grouper were described many years ago by Dr. C. H. Townsend, at that time Director of the New York Aquarium. "In one," he wrote, "the fish is uniformly dark; in another creamy white. In a third it is dark above with white under parts. In a fourth the upper part is sharply banded, the lower pure white. A fifth phase shows dark bands, the whole fish taking on a light brown coloration. While in a sixth the fish is pale, with all dark markings tending to disappear. The seventh phase shows a light-colored fish with the whole body sharply banded and mottled with black." The eighth, and rarer, color change gives the grouper a dusky hue above, white below, with a median black band from head to tail.

The Nassau Grouper ranges from North Carolina throughout the West Indies and south to Brazil and is quite often seen in tropical food markets. It may weigh 50 pounds.

Some groupers attain immense size; the Giant Grouper of Florida to tropical South America on both coasts goes to 750 pounds and the Queensland Grouper of the Great Barrier Reef and elsewhere in the Indo-Pacific is reported to reach 1,000 pounds. Shell divers have learned to keep out of its way, for it is known to stalk them and make an attack rush.

Surf casting for Striped Bass is an often rewarding sport along the Atlantic coast from the Gulf of St. Lawrence to northern Florida, and there is also a large commercial take of the fish. *Striped Bass* Late in the last century Striped Bass were shipped to California,

Nassau Grouper
Giant Grouper

and now they are abundant from southern California to Washington. A huge 125-pounder was caught off North Carolina, but 78 pounds is the record for California. This species is now being propagated in hatcheries for stocking in lakes and reservoirs. In nature, the Striped Bass spends most of its life in the sea, but ascends rivers to spawn.

Bright colors give distinction to some of the smaller members of the family, such as the finely spotted Red Hind that reaches northward to the Carolinas. Another excellent food fish is the Black Sea Bass of Cape Ann to northern Florida, usually found well offshore and over rocky bottoms. It weighs up to 8 pounds.

The foot-long White Perch is one of several species that inhabit both brackish and fresh water; at one time it was common in park lakes in New York City.

Among the family's oddities are the Soapfish and the Freckled Soapfish whose mucous coverings give off a sudslike *See page 108* foam when they are handled. The Soapfish ranges from Florida to Brazil.

ABOVE: *Red Hind*
OPPOSITE: *White Perch*

Freckled Soapfish
Aholehole

Aholeholes
PERCIFORMES: KUHLIIDAE

The Hawaiian Aholehole (pronounced "A-holy-holy") is a silvery, foot-long, hardy little food fish abounding around the Hawaiian Islands. There are about a dozen species in the Indo-Pacific region, mostly marine, but some in brackish and fresh waters. The ease with which they can be transported by air has made them familiar in many aquariums in the United States.

Tripletail
PERCIFORMES: LOBOTIDAE

The large and rounded dorsal and anal fins of the Tripletail, together with the actual tail fin, give it the appearance of having three tails—hence its common name. Tripletails of the tropical Atlantic and Indo-Pacific inhabit salt, brackish, or even fresh water. The Atlantic Tripletail wanders to Cape Cod and is sometimes taken in New York Bay in summer.

Adults are almost uniformly black, up to 40 inches long, and weigh 30 or 40 pounds. They are a food fish. Young Tripletails have a variety of colors—tan, yellowish, mottled—and conceal themselves by turning sideways and floating like leaves.

Tripletail

Snappers
PERCIFORMES: LUTJANIDAE

Snappers are highly prized as food fishes in many parts of the tropics. Indeed, the Red Snapper has been called the most important tropical fish that comes to the United States market. There are many kinds of snappers, and they are often brilliantly colored and of good size, up to 2 or 3 feet long.

The Red Snapper of the West Indies to Florida is unmistakable among snappers because of its almost uniform scarlet color. Distinctive, too, is the 2-foot Yellowtail so popular in Cuba, where it is called Rabirubia; above, the fish is bluish with yellow spots, and a bright yellow band extends from the tail to the eye. It is abundant around Key West and south to Brazil and in the eastern tropical Atlantic.

Although they are primarily tropical fishes (in the Indo-Pacific as well as in the Atlantic), some snappers regularly or occasionally range well into the temperate seas. The comparatively unspectacular Gray Snapper, mostly greenish, is taken off New Jersey, although it is much more abundant from the Florida

See page 112

Mutton Snapper

Keys and the West Indies to Brazil. The richly colored School- *See page 112*
master wanders north to Massachusetts when young, and the big
Mutton Snapper (up to 25 pounds) has been taken off Cape Cod.
Like the Schoolmaster, its more usual home is from Florida to
Brazil.

Bigeyes
PERCIFORMES: PRIACANTHIDAE

One of the most brilliant tropical fishes entering the tem-
perate Atlantic is the Bigeye, or Catalufa, found on both sides of   *See page 112*
the ocean. It is bright crimson, with extremely large eyes that
have a golden glint and the peculiar optical quality of seeming
to reflect bright aquarium lights upward. A former Director of the
New York Aquarium wrote that "if viewed from above, especially in slightly turbid water, shafts of light strike upward to the
surface like the beams of miniature searchlights."

Bigeyes feed on other fishes and are most active at night
along the bottom. The Bigeye of the Atlantic from Brazil to
Rhode Island reaches 14 inches.

Cardinalfishes
PERCIFORMES: APOGONIDAE

The small cardinalfishes of the tropical Atlantic and the
Indo-Pacific, generally scarlet or copper-colored, are rather
secretive, and one of them is known as the Conchfish from its
habit of taking shelter in the mantle cavity of conchs. Other
members of the family hide in sponges and other cavities.

All the cardinalfishes are small, with 8 inches the maximum
and most under 4 inches. One of the small ones is the Flamefish,   *See page 114*
found from Florida to Brazil, but occasionally straggling north to
Massachusetts. It is almost entirely bright red. The Conchfish is
about 2 inches long. The males of many species carry the eggs in
their mouths.

Sunfishes and Black Basses
PERCIFORMES: CENTRARCHIDAE

A bent pin, a piece of string, a willow pole, and a can of
"fishing worms" are the traditional (but not really very efficient)
equipment for catching sunfishes; fishing for the basses takes
more sophisticated tackle and greater skill. Either way the sunfish-bass family provides sport throughout the United States.

It is a North American family, originally inhabiting almost
any fresh water east of the Rockies, but now introduced in every
state except Alaska. Some seventy common names, used locally,
have been recorded for the sunfishes, but the Pumpkinseed (or   *See pages 114-115*
Common Sunfish), Bluegill, Longear Sunfish, Blackbanded Sun-   *See pages 113-115*
fish, Redbreast Sunfish, Black Crappie, and White Crappie are

ABOVE: *Bigeye*

RIGHT: *Gray Snapper*

BELOW: *Schoolmaster*

Bluegills in a winter aggregation;
strings indicate the flow of the current

Flamefish

*Pumpkinseed,
or Common Sunfish,
on nest*

See page 116
See page 117

species that would be generally recognized under those names. There is even a Pygmy Sunfish in the Florida Everglades, mature at 1 inch and never exceeding 1½ inches. On the other hand, a Largemouth Bass 32½ inches long and weighing 22 pounds 4 ounces was taken in Georgia in 1932, and a Smallmouth Bass 27 inches long and weighing 11 pounds 15 ounces was pulled out of a lake straddling Kentucky and Tennessee in 1955. Most fishermen are content with much smaller sizes.

The sunfish-bass family is carnivorous and feeds on worms,

leeches, land and water insects and their larvae, crayfish, and—
the larger species—on other and smaller fishes. In the summer
spawning season the male prepares a nest, a shallow basin in
sand, induces one or more females to deposit eggs there, and
then fertilizes them. The nest may be in 1 to 5 feet of clear water.
The male guards the nest and the fry after the eggs have hatched
in a few days. The female pays neither eggs nor fry any further
attention after her work is done.

The Pumpkinseed seldom exceeds 4 to 6 inches in small

TOP:
Blackbanded Sunfish
ABOVE:
Pumpkinseed,
or Common Sunfish.
GIUSEPPE MAZZA
PHOTO.

streams, but in larger ones may grow to 8 or 9 inches. For a small freshwater fish it is quite colorful, an iridescent mingling of orange and red, yellow, blue, and green, in spots and bars; it can always be recognized by the bright red spot on the "ear flap," an extension at the rear of the gill cover.

The Bluegill is not quite so colorful, but is still strongly barred and has a bluish cast on the lower jaw and the lower edge of the cheek and gill cover. Very rarely it weighs 4 pounds or a little more. It can be caught in winter by fishing through the ice in northern lakes.

Two other very colorful sunfishes are the Longear, so called from the long extension of its ear flap, from the Southeast and the Mississippi Valley, and the Redbreast of clear streams from Maine to Louisiana.

Some of the smaller sunfishes, such as the Blackbanded, are favorites in home aquariums; German breeders ship them all over the world.

Because they are such excellent game fishes, the basses have been stocked in streams and ponds and lakes all over the country. Any bass fisherman will argue with any other bass fisherman about the fighting qualities of the Largemouth vs. the Smallmouth.

Largemouth Bass

OPPOSITE: *Smallmouth Bass in a winter aggregation*

Perches, Walleyes, and Darters
PERCIFORMES: PERCIDAE

The Yellow Perch and the Walleye are important food fishes over much of North America, from the southern third of Canada to Mexico and all across the United States to the Rockies. Anglers take large numbers, but the catch by commercial fisheries, particularly in the Great Lakes, amounts to millions of pounds annually.

The darters, on the other hand, are among the smallest of

North American fishes, most from 1 to 3 inches long, and while many of them are brilliantly colored, especially in the breeding season, they have no food importance. They are not even well known to most fishermen.

The Yellow Perch, averaging 6 to 8 inches in length in shallow waters and 14 to 15 inches in deeper lakes, has a greenish yellow back and sides marked with six to nine dark vertical bars. The female lays strings of sticky eggs, in a kind of ribbon that may be 2 to 7 feet long. These stick to water vegetation along the shore and are not guarded. Insects and their larvae, crayfish, and smaller fishes are the usual food.

The Walleye gets its name from the fact that its large eyes are rather opaque, so that the fish seems to be blind. Greenish brown on the back, with rather mottled brassy sides, a distinguishing mark is the largish black mottling on the posterior part of the dorsal fin. The usual size in streams is 1 to 3 pounds, 10 to 15 pounds is occasional in the Great Lakes, and a whopper weighing 25 pounds was taken from a lake in Tennessee in 1960. Fishing through the ice for Walleyes is a cold but rewarding sport in northern lakes. This is another fish that does not guard its eggs, but scatters them over a rocky or gravelly bottom. One female may lay from twenty thousand to half a million eggs.

Most of the darters are bottom-dwellers, and some even bury themselves and lie quietly until something impels them to dart forward a few inches. They feed on minute insect larvae and tiny crustaceans. The abundant Johnny Darter, about 2½ inches long, lays its eggs under shelving rocks and works upside-down to do it. The male guards and aerates the eggs.

Bluefish
PERCIFORMES: POMATOMIDAE

It is only fair, perhaps, that a fish that enjoys eating as much as the Bluefish does should itself be eaten with great enjoyment by human beings. The Bluefish rather overdoes things, however; it goes on killing when it can eat no more out of sheer repletion and has been compared by various writers to the voracious Piranha, to "an animated chopping machine," and schools of Bluefish to "a pack of hungry wolves."

See page 120

There is only one species, of temperate and tropical waters around the world except in the central and eastern Pacific. Casting for Bluefish is an excellent sport on beaches around New York and Long Island, and when they are present in large numbers — as when they are feeding on shoals of Menhaden — fishermen often have to call in the neighbors to get rid of their catch.

The name comes from the bluish green color. The maximum weight is about 27 pounds.

Bluefish

Jacks, Pompano, and Relatives
PERCIFORMES: CARANGIDAE

There are a number of highly prized food fishes in this marine family of tropical and temperate waters—the Pompano, for example. There are some two hundred species, a few of which go into fresh water.

See page 122 The Atlantic Pompano, about 18 inches long and weighing 2 pounds, ranges from Cape Cod to the Gulf coast and is plentiful around Florida; only the young are likely to be seen north of Virginia. A relative, though not so highly prized for food, is the *See page 123* Palometa of coastal waters from Virginia to Brazil; it is about 1 foot long.

One of the larger members of the family in Atlantic waters *Crevalle Jack* is the Crevalle Jack, up to 2½ feet long and a weight of 20 pounds. It occasionally wanders up to Massachusetts and is also known in the eastern Pacific.

The tall, thin, silvery body of the Lookdown, with its eyes placed extraordinarily high above the mouth, gives a ready clue

Young Atlantic
Pompano
OPPOSITE: *Palometa*

Lookdown, or Silvery Moonfish; below, Jackknifefish
found from Bermuda and the Carolinas to Brazil (Sciaenidae).

to its names—Lookdown and Silvery Moonfish. Primarily it is a fish of tropical waters, and only the young are apt to wander as far north as Cape Cod. It reaches a length of about 1 foot.

Another interesting tropical fish that appears in local waters in summertime—always as a juvenile—is the Threadfish, in which the first rays of the dorsal and anal fins are lengthened into thin threads that are sometimes much longer than the fish's body. They grow shorter with age. Threadfish have been captured locally for exhibition.

Dolphins
PERCIFORMES: CORYPHAENIDAE

"The dying dolphin's changing hues" have been celebrated in poetry and remarked by everyone who has pulled this beautiful game fish out of the sea. A prismatic sequence of changes begins when the fish is captured, and its gold, green, and blue body rapidly assumes less brilliant colors until at death it is olive drab.

Dolphins—not to be confused with the aquatic mammal also called Dolphin—are fish of the high seas around the world. There are only two species, the Dolphin and the Pompano Dolphin. The Dolphin attains a length of 5 feet; the Pompano

Juvenile Dolphin.
Adult Dolphin.
WOMETCO MIAMI
SEAQUARIUM PHOTOS.

125

Dolphin, 12 to 30 inches. They are very fast swimmers, and the Dolphin has been clocked at 37 miles an hour. This perhaps accounts for the Dolphin's ability to feed on flyingfishes.

Grunts
PERCIFORMES: POMADASYIDAE

Grunts actually do make grunting sounds — hence their name. They do so by grinding together the teeth in the throat, the sound being amplified by the gasbladder. They are widely distributed in the tropical western Atlantic, and some are beautifully colored.

One of the showiest bears the unlovely name of Porkfish; its foot-long blue body bears horizontal golden stripes, the tail is orange-yellow, and dark vertical streaks run through the eyes and just behind the gills. It is a common fish from Florida to

Porkfish.
BELOW LEFT AND
OPPOSITE.

Brazil. Juveniles are among the "cleaner-fishes," spending much *Bluestripe Grunt*
time picking parasites from other fishes.

Equally pretty is the French Grunt of about the same range
and of the same size, with electric blue stripes running horizontally on the sides and diagonally on the back.

The Bluestripe Grunt of Florida and the West Indies to
Brazil reaches a length of about 18 inches. Like some other
grunts, two Bluestripes will often approach each other with the
mouth wide open to display the bright red interior and will then
shove each other with the mouth—possibly to assert territory or
perhaps as a courtship gesture.

Croakers
PERCIFORMES: SCIAENIDAE

Croakers produce their extraordinary repertory of creaking,
drumming, purring, and whistling sounds by means of muscles
attached to the gasbladder; their vibrations of about twenty-four
times a second are transmitted to the walls of the gasbladder,
which acts as a resonance box. Croakers have been heard by
persons 6 feet above the surface while the fish were at a depth
of 70 feet.

OPPOSITE: *Bluestripe Grunts in "kissing" posture.* CARLETON RAY PHOTO.

Red Drum, or Channel Bass
Spot, or Lafayette. WOMETCO MIAMI SEAQUARIUM PHOTO.

There are about 160 species, most in shallow coastal waters of the warm and temperate seas, some associated with coral reefs, and a few exclusively in fresh water. Many of them are excellent food fishes.

Along the American Atlantic coast the Weakfish (also called Sea Trout or Squeteague) is of great commercial value, and millions of pounds are harvested every year. The usual weight is 5 to 6 pounds. The name is said to come from its soft mouth, so that a hook easily tears out.

One of the best-known croakers is called the Black Drum — adults are usually dark gray, although the young bear dark vertical bands. Some reach a length of 4 feet and a weight of 146 pounds, and since they feed largely on shellfish, they are a menace to oyster beds.

The Atlantic Croaker is sporadically abundant along the Atlantic and Gulf coasts and can be caught with hook and line; it is about a foot long. Another excellent food fish in this family is the Red Drum, or Channel Bass, weighing up to 83 pounds. It is found along sandy shores from Massachusetts to Texas, but is rare north of Virginia.

An odd thing about the Spot (distinguished by a dark spot at the base of the pectoral fin and black bars up the back above the lateral line) is its variation in abundance. At intervals of some years there have been "invasions" of vast numbers of Spots in local waters. One of those peaks came during the Revolutionary War, and the fish were thus called Lafayettes, in honor of General Lafayette — a name that is still sometimes used. Spots, or Lafayettes, reach a length of about 12 inches.

Not all members of the croaker family are noisy. The Northern Kingfish, found from Florida to Massachusetts but rare north of Virginia, has no gasbladder and is virtually voiceless. It is a bottom-feeder on crabs, squid, shrimp, worms, and young fish and weighs 2 to 3 pounds.

See page 132

The Freshwater Drum is the only exclusively freshwater sciaenid and lives in lakes and rivers from Canada to Central America. It makes typical croaker noises, and in the Deep South it is called "Thunderpumper."

Goatfishes
PERCIFORMES: MULLIDAE

It is likely that goatfishes earned their name from the pair of long and flexible barbels under the chin — reminiscent of a billy goat's whiskers. Typically the goatfishes swim along the bottom, barbels advanced and waggling to stir up the sand and find small bits of food. They are inshore fishes of tropical and temperate seas, and many are brilliantly colored. They are also known as surmullets, but the true mullets are in another family.

131

Northern Kingfish

Spotted Goatfish

Goatfishes are famed for their rapid changes of color in life and death; in ancient Roman times they were brought to the table in glass dishes so that the guests could enjoy the kaleidoscope of colors as they died. Modern Hawaiian fishermen ice them immediately after they are caught to retain their red color, for red fishes are highly prized in the Islands.

Along the Atlantic coast are found the Red Goatfish of the West Indies and Florida, straggling north to New York; the red-blotched Spotted Goatfish of Florida and the West Indies, which can make its red disappear in a few minutes; and the largely yellow Yellow Goatfish of the Florida-West Indies region. These are small fishes, 8 inches to about a foot long. They travel singly or in schools and feed on invertebrates.

Porgies

PERCIFORMES: SPARIDAE

Goatfish of the Indo-Pacific. (Mullidae).

Shellfish are a major part of the diet of the porgy family, and it is characteristic of porgies to have heavy, molarlike teeth that are used to crush shells. There are about one hundred species, fourteen along the Atlantic coast and others around South Africa, Australia, Japan, the Mediterranean, northern Europe, South America, and Hawaii.

Scup, or Northern Porgy

The Scup, or Northern Porgy, is a food fish of importance from Maine to South Carolina and is readily caught on hand lines; it is also taken commercially. A length of about 16 inches and a weight of 2 pounds are usual. The larger Sheepshead, sometimes weighing 20 pounds, occurs from Cape Cod to Texas, but for some reason it is not now abundant in New York waters. It is also a good food fish. The 10-inch Pinfish is appreciated as food in Florida and the Gulf waters, but is not plentiful north of Delaware.

Sheepshead

Pinfish

ABOVE: *Archerfish taking aim at an insect*

OPPOSITE: *The Archerfish's "water bullet" strikes its insect prey.*
The prey is brought down and the Archerfish seizes it.

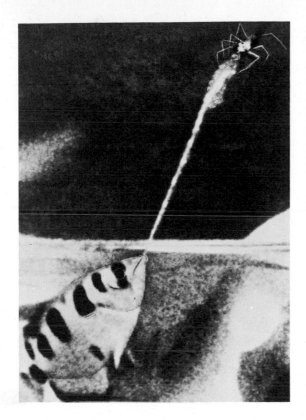

Archerfishes

PERCIFORMES: TOXOTIDAE

Fishes have many strange ways of securing food, but a fish that spits water bullets at its prey is surely in a class by itself. The Archerfish of southeastern Asia and Australia is able to perform this feat by pressing its tongue against a groove in the roof of the mouth to form a sort of rifle barrel and then forcefully compressing the gill covers so that a series of drops of water is expelled.

The Archerfish rises to the surface to take aim and can hit an insect on a leaf or plant stem at a distance of 3 feet; the drenching usually knocks the prey into the water, where it is seized by the fish's mouth. Individuals vary greatly in their accuracy with water pellets and the number of "rounds" they can fire.

Archerfishes (there are four species) do not depend entirely on shooting their food down, however, and a good part of their diet probably consists of floating aquatic organisms that they take in the usual way while swimming.

The maximum size of the Archerfish most commonly exhibited is about 7½ inches. Color is variable, but often yellowish green to brown, with broad dark saddle markings across the back and sides.

Atlantic Spadefish

Spadefishes
PERCIFORMES: EPHIPPIDAE

See page 138

Spadefishes are essentially tropical marine fishes of the Americas and West Africa, but the Atlantic Spadefish ranges as far north as Cape Cod. Deep-bodied and thin, it is strongly marked when young with vertical dark bands that disappear as it reaches its maximum size of about 3 feet and weight of 20 pounds. It can change color almost instantly, assuming an all-white, all-black, or banded pattern.

Spadefishes are a food fish in the tropics and have been successfully introduced into Bermuda waters. They feed chiefly on invertebrates and somehow find sustenance in such insubstantial, watery fare as comb-jellies and the Portuguese Man-of-War.

Rudderfishes, or Sea Chubs
PERCIFORMES: KYPHOSIDAE

From the stern of a ship in tropical Atlantic waters a school of fishes may sometimes be seen following close behind for distances of up to hundreds of miles. These are the rudderfishes, members of a small family of about a dozen species.

The Bermuda Chub is a well-known rudderfish, common along the Florida Keys, Bermuda, and the West Indies generally and in summer ranging north to Cape Cod. Like so many tropical fishes, it can change color instantly; at one moment it may be steel gray with horizontal light and dark lines, and at the next marked with white spots. It reaches a length of about 18 inches.

Scats
PERCIFORMES: SCATOPHAGIDAE

Young scats are lively and peaceful inhabitants of many home aquariums — their chief fault is that they nibble on the plants in the tank — and are prized for their striking patterns of spots and streaks. There are about half a dozen species, found in

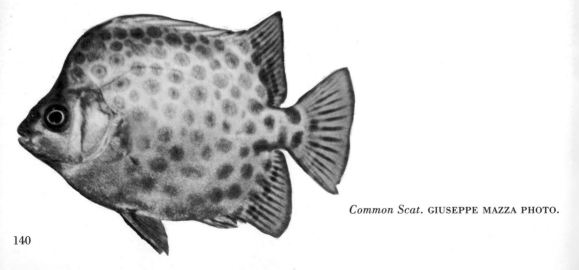

Common Scat. GIUSEPPE MAZZA PHOTO.

Bermuda Chub

coastal and brackish waters of south and southeastern Asia and around Australia. It is believed that scats spawn around coral reefs and that the young then enter fresh or brackish water.

They reach a length of 12 inches in their native waters, but only about half that under home-aquarium conditions. They are at their prettiest when about 2½ inches long; with increasing age the orange-red of the back fades out, at least in the Common Scat.

The scientific name of the scats means "dung eater." Schools of them can usually be found around the sewer outlets of cities, and they feed on almost any kind of decaying refuse.

Angelfishes and Butterflyfishes
PERCIFORMES: CHAETODONTIDAE

Angelfishes and butterflyfishes are remarkable for their beauty, even in the gaudy world of tropical reefs where every fantasy of color and form seems to be realized in the fishes, anemones, corals, and sponges.

There are about 150 species in the shallow tropical seas of the world. The general body form in the family is disk-shaped and strongly compressed. The mouth is small and may be at the end of a snoutlike extension—particularly noticeable in the Long-nosed Butterflyfish—and is well adapted to seeking out small invertebrates in coral crevices. Butterflyfishes are seldom

Long-nosed Butterflyfish, or Forcepsfish

Foureye Butterflyfish

longer than 6 or 8 inches, but some of the angels reach a length of 2 feet.

Although they are typically associated with coral reefs, they are not confined to that habitat; some Atlantic species such as the Spotfin Butterflyfish, the Foureye Butterflyfish, and the French Angelfish occasionally wander as far north as Massachusetts.

The Foureye takes its name from the large dark spot, outlined in white, near the tail—an "eye" much more prominent than the actual eye hardly visible in the dark streak that runs across the head. A predator might well mistake the spot as marking the forward part of the body and be deceived by the direction the fish takes when it darts away.

The Queen Angelfish of the West Indies and Florida reaches a length of about 2 feet and is a good food fish. It is one of the showiest of the larger angels, predominantly yellow and blue.

"Forcepsfish" is another name for the Long-nosed Butterflyfish—an obvious name, for its mouth is at the end of a long, slender snout. It is a fish of the Indo-Pacific tropical reefs.

Air shipment makes it possible nowadays for brilliant fishes of the tropical Pacific to be seen in almost any part of the world, so that the many-streaked Barred Butterflyfish, the black, yellow, and white Fourspot Butterflyfish, and the orange and black Raccoon Butterflyfish are commonly exhibited. Another small beauty is the Potter's Angelfish of Hawaii, of luminous red and black, only 4 inches long.

BELOW: *Four-spot Butterflyfish of the Indo-Pacific. (Chaetodontidae).*

See page 147 for other fish

Many young angelfishes bear little resemblance to the adults. In the Imperial Angelfish of the Indo-Pacific, for example, the young have a bizarre pattern of concentric white and blue lines and white-outlined spots, but the adults are streaked with oblique yellowish lines on the purplish-brown body.

Still, the Indo-Pacific does not have it all its own way as far as color is concerned; certainly the yellow and black Rock Beauty of Florida to Rio de Janeiro stands out in any collection of tropical fishes, for its pattern is bold, and it grows to a length of more than 1 foot.

Imperial Angelfish in adult coloration

OPPOSITE: *Young
Queen Angelfish*

RIGHT:
*Potter's Angelfish of
Hawaiian waters.
(Chaetodontidae).*

*Barred Butterflyfish
of the Indo-Pacific.
(Chaetodontidae).*

*Young French
Angelfish*

147

Leaffishes

PERCIFORMES: NANDIDAE

Mimicry and camouflage are old dodges in the animal kingdom, and one of the expert practitioners is the famous Leaffish of the fresh waters in tropical South America. It is thin, leaf-shaped, leaf-colored, and it even has a fleshy barbel on its chin that looks like a leaf stem. It may be 4 inches long.

Its color and pattern change to match its surroundings; in green plants along a river's edge it is greenish; among dead and floating leaves it becomes as brown and mottled as they are. Drifting through open water at a head-down angle, it moves as slowly as a leaf would move in the current — except that the Leaffish is propelling itself in quiet water by the almost invisible motions of its transparent fins. Seeking food at the surface, it turns on its side and becomes a floating leaf. If a fish — even one half as large as it is — approaches within an inch, the tapering mouth behind the "stem" suddenly opens, a membranous oval tunnel pops out, and in a flash the prey is drawn in. A vacuum sweeper could do it no better.

Leaffishes are popular in home aquariums and can be easily kept if plenty of small fishes are provided as their food, for they are voracious feeders. Another hobby fish in the same family is the Badis, or Chameleonfish, which can change color rapidly.

The family has a curious distribution: South America, Africa, and Southeast Asia.

RIGHT: *Leaffish*

OPPOSITE:
Black-chinned Mouthbreeder of West Africa. In this species the male incubates the eggs in his mouth. (Cichlidae).

Discus at right, above

Cichlids
PERCIFORMES: CICHLIDAE

The freshwater cichlids of tropical South America north to Texas and of Africa are a large family of some six hundred species. Home aquarists may appreciate the family for the many contributions it has made to their tanks, but millions of the world's protein-starved people thank it for the Tilapia, a fast-growing and prolific food fish that thrives in almost any fresh or brackish warm water.

"Scalare" and "Angelfish" are names used interchangeably for one of the most striking home-aquarium cichlids, notable for its very high dorsal and anal fins and bold vertical bands. It comes from the Amazon and Orinoco basins. Several interesting varieties, such as the Black Angel and the Veil Angel, have been developed. *See pages 152–153*

The Discus of the Amazon Basin and the Rio Negro and its tributaries created a sensation when it was introduced in the early 1930's. Thin and disklike, its chocolate brown body is handsomely striped with wavy blue lines. The breeding habits of the Discus are especially interesting, for after the eggs hatch, the parents transfer the tiny fish to underwater plant stems and leaves and take turns fanning them. In two or three days they attach themselves by short threads to the body of one of the parents and feed on a mucous secretion of the skin. When one parent wants a rest from juvenile grazing, it gives a vigorous flick of the tail and scatters the young; the other parent swims to them and takes over the job of providing pasturage.

The Firemouth of northern Yucatan is an easily recognized cichlid, for the male has a red mouth, chin, and belly that are most intensely colored in the breeding season, in strong contrast to the dark and bluish gray back and sides and dark bars and stripes.

The Tilapia takes its name from the genus to which it belongs; there are dozens of others in the genus, but *Tilapia mossambica* is the East African species so widely introduced through Indonesia, Hawaii, and the West Indies and the one generally understood when the name is given. It was accidentally introduced into Java in the late 1930's and quickly became so popular as a food fish that plantings were made throughout the Old World and New World tropics. Its production of young and its rate of growth are phenomenal: fifty Tilapias planted in a tiny pond less than one-fiftieth of an acre in extent produced thirty-five hundred young in six months. And since Tilapias breed throughout the year, the fry need no special attention, and both adults and young will eat anything from table scraps to algae and plankton, the economic importance of the fish can hardly be exaggerated.

Angelfish, or Scalare

Tilapia

Tilapia is a mouthbrooder. The male scoops out a small depression on the bottom, and the eggs are deposited and fertilized there. The female then takes them in her mouth and holds them and the young for about three weeks.

Tilapias are not really the "miracle fish" that they were said to be during the first enthusiasm for introducing them throughout the tropics; for one thing, overcrowding in small ponds stunts their growth. But in favorable situations they attain a weight of 1 pound in eight months, or in exceptional circumstances 2 pounds in the first year.

Damselfishes
PERCIFORMES: POMACENTRIDAE

When a small fish is careless enough to swim into a sea anemone's thicket of tentacles, it generally pays for the error with its life. Those soft, gently waving protrusions suddenly discharge a battery of stinging cells, and the numbed and dying fish is passed inexorably toward the mouth opening.

154

OPPOSITE: *Two-stripe Damselfish*

Clown Anemonefish in close association with a sea anemone

And yet, a few inches away, another small fish may be nestled among the tentacles or swimming in and out with nonchalance. This might be a Clown Anemonefish of the Indo-Pacific, one of about a dozen species of damselfish that can live in a close relationship with sea anemones because of a mucous secretion that prevents the stinging discharge. Its common name was a happy inspiration, for it does irresistibly remind one of a clown: orange-brown body set off by a white collar, band around the middle, and another band around the base of the black-edged tail.

Damselfishes are found in all shallow tropical seas and in the cool waters off the coast of southern California. They are typically reef fishes, and most are beautiful—such as the Blue Reeffish, or Blue Chromis, of an iridescent blue color, the Yellowtail Damselfish whose young lack the yellow tail but make up for it by a sprinkling of sky blue spots, and the blue and yellow Beaugregory of Bermuda, the West Indies, and Florida. Like most damselfishes, all these are small, about 6 inches maximum.

The Sergeant Major is often seen around wharves and reefs in Florida and the West Indies—but not always looking the same at all times, for it can almost instantaneously change from a yellow fish with heavy black bands to a silvery or black fish. It is

See page 159

See page 159

*Blue Reeffish,
or Blue Chromis*

TEXT CONTINUED ON PAGE 161

157

*Young Yellowtail
Damselfish*

Sergeant Major
OPPOSITE:
*Three-stripe
Damselfish*

Rainbow Wrasse preparing to clean a Blue Reeffish

Bird Wrasse of the Indo-Pacific. (Labridae).

found on both sides of the Atlantic and in the Pacific. Like many other damselfishes, it spends much of its time patrolling the small area it has made its own by vigorously driving away other fishes, especially other Sergeant Majors. Unless an aquarium tank is large, only one Sergeant Major can be kept in it.

Small, brightly colored fishes are always in need of hiding places, and coral heads are made to order for the damselfishes. Coral convolutions may not be as safe as sea anemone tentacles — long-snouted fishes can get at them — but they are better than nothing, and whole schools of the Two-stripe and Three-stripe *See page 158* Damselfish and the Two-spot Damselfish of the Indo-Pacific are likely to be seen circling slowly over the corals, ready to streak for "home" if frightened.

Wrasses
PERCIFORMES: LABRIDAE

Many of the small wrasses of tropical seas are well known for the parasite-removing service they perform for large fishes. With quick nibbles they move around the body, the eyes, and the gills, and even enter the open mouth of such predators as groupers, snappers, moray eels, and parrotfishes — and the big fish seem to enjoy it. Indeed, such fishes deliberately swim into a "service station" and wait patiently to be cleaned.

Some years ago the New York Aquarium received several 3-inch Rainbow Wrasses from the Indo-Pacific. These electric blue and black wrasses are much different in appearance from their tropical Atlantic relatives, and so it was with some trepidation that the Aquarium introduced them into a tank containing Atlantic groupers and moray eels — fishes that could never have seen a Rainbow Wrasse before. The Director of the Aquarium subsequently reported: "Within five minutes all the groupers were lying on the bottom of the tank, mouths wide open, gill covers extended, and all lay quietly while the tiny wrasses swam over and under, in the gills and out the mouth."

The presumption is that there is some characteristic behavior pattern in wrasses that their "customers" recognize.

Wrasses have many other peculiarities — as might be expected in a family of about six hundred species. One is the difference in color between young and adults and between males and females of the numerous species. The West Indian Bluehead, for example, is a lovely lemon yellow as a juvenile and may also have a wide black stripe along the sides. Some adult males have a clear blue head and immediately behind it two black bands separated by a white band — and the rest of the body is moss green. Even the tail changes and becomes a deep crescent. It is small wonder that there has been much confusion in the naming of wrasses.

161

Bluehead

Long-jawed Wrasse.
The jaws are slightly
extended as the fish
swallows a 3-inch
Killie.

162

Fishes have various sleeping postures; the wrasses usually lie on the bottom on their sides. Some species bury themselves in sand at the bottom of an aquarium tank, and the Rainbow Wrasse secretes a mucous cocoon about its body at night.

All the wrasses are carnivores, and one, the Long-jawed Wrasse of the Indo-Pacific, has a method unique among wrasses for taking its prey. The 13-inch Long-jaw can protrude its jaws for about 2 inches — which means that it can approach a small fish and "strike" from an unexpected distance.

Some of the larger wrasses are food fishes. The Tautog, 3 feet long and up to 22 pounds in weight, is common between Cape Cod and Delaware, and farther south, from Florida through the West Indies, the 2-foot Hogfish is also considered good eating. It can change color and pattern almost instantly. Another pretty wrasse is the Spanish Hogfish of Florida and the West Indies, violet-red above and yellow-orange below. One of the commonest wrasses in the reefs of Florida and the West Indies is the Slippery Dick, usually less than 6 inches long.

See page 165

Male Hogfish in adult coloration

Slippery Dick

Parrotfishes
PERCIFORMES: SCARIDAE

The parrotfishes of tropical seas have been described as "grazing on underwater plants and algae like herds of gaudy cows." There is no denying their gaudiness, and they do graze on coral reefs and bite off bits of coral as they feed, but to make the simile complete we would have to imagine cows with parrot-like mouths; the parrotfishes have prominent jaw teeth more or less fused so that they resemble the beak of a parrot.

Like the wrasses, they also have platelike throat teeth, and these are used to grind up the coral torn off when they feed on the organisms growing on the surface of the reef. Most of the parrotfishes of West Indian and Florida waters are about 1 foot long; the colorful Rainbow Parrotfish—olive green, each scale edged with brown, green markings on the head, and the under parts reddish—is the largest of the parrotfishes in this area and

Stoplight Parrotfish

reaches 3 feet. It can easily cut through a fishhook with its bright blue beak.

In the Indo-Pacific some parrotfish reach a length of 6 feet, and others 12 feet long have been reported.

One of the most brilliant West Indies-to-Florida species is the Stoplight Parrotfish, a little more than a foot long, with a red crescent at the base of the caudal fin, a yellow spot on the gill covers, and a green band next to the red crescent.

Some of the parrotfishes — like the Rainbow Wrasse — form a mucous envelope about their bodies at night. It takes about half an hour for the envelope to form, but the fish can escape from it quickly in an emergency.

Parrotfishes undergo dramatic changes of color as they mature, some as many as three times, and males and females also may be quite different in coloration. This has led to a great deal of confusion in the identification of species, and one authority was able to reduce the original enormous number of 350 named "species" to a mere eighty. Even that number may be too high.

Jawfishes
PERCIFORMES: OPISTOGNATHIDAE

There are few fishes in an Aquarium more fascinating to watch than Yellowhead Jawfishes. Many fishes seem to spend their time swimming aimlessly, but the Yellowhead Jawfishes keep busy with household chores — excavating and cleaning their tunnels in the sandy bottom, chasing away intruders, carrying bits of rock and shell and sand in their capacious mouths, spitting sand, descending tailfirst into their burrows, rising and sinking in a dreamy ballet.

See page 168

The Yellowhead belongs to a small family known in the Florida-Bermuda-West Indies waters and also in the Indo-African region, the Yellowhead itself coming from the West Indies. It is about 3½ inches long, pale yellow around the head, and the rest of the body is a satiny light blue. Its most usual posture is diagonally vertical as it holds its position over the burrow it has excavated in the sand, but oddly enough its eyes are set horizontally and can even be rotated to maintain the horizontal position no matter what the attitude of the body.

The burrows are 12 to 14 inches deep, in open sand or among low aquatic vegetation, and the little fishes excavate them by scooping up sand, small stones, and bits of shell and coral in their mouths. The burrows are lined with stones to keep them from caving in, and a tiny jawfish can carry a stone three-fourths of an inch in diameter. Other jawfishes that intrude on the home territory are quickly chased away by what is presumed to be threatening gestures — erection of the fins and flaring of the gill covers. Nevertheless, at least in the Aquarium's tanks, there is much raiding of one another's pile of stones at the lip of the burrows, and mock battles constantly occur.

At least three species of jawfish are known to be mouth-brooders.

Yellowhead Jawfish

Stargazers
PERCIFORMES: URANOSCOPIDAE

There are many traps for the unwary in the ocean, and the stargazers of tropical and temperate seas are adept at setting some effective ones. Some species have electric organs bunched behind the eyes and formed of specialized optical tissue; these can give off discharges of as much as 50 volts. They have dangerous venom spines behind the gill cover. Some have little fleshy tabs that can be projected from the mouth to lure small fishes within range as the stargazer lies buried in sand.

Actually, it is not known whether the electrical discharge is for the purpose of stunning prey or has a different function, but the concealed position of the fish, with only the head and mouth projecting is certainly a trap. In all stargazers the eyes are placed close together on top of the flat head and stare upward — hence their name.

In western Atlantic waters the Northern Stargazer ranges from New York Bay to Virginia; a big one may be 22 inches long and weigh 20 pounds. Farther south, to Brazil, is the Southern Stargazer. Neither has fishing lures, but this device is found in the European Stargazer. The usual prey is crustaceans and small fishes.

Southern Stargazer.
WOMETCO MIAMI
SEAQUARIUM PHOTO.

Moorish Idol
PERCIFORMES: ZANCLIDAE

As if its vivid vertical stripes and medium-long snout were not enough to call attention to it in an aquarium tank, the long and backward-sweeping dorsal fin of the Moorish Idol marks it as an unusual fish. Yellow and black, with blue, white, and red "trimmings," it is one of the most spectacular fishes of the Indo-Pacific reefs, where spectacular fishes abound. It reaches a length of about 7 inches.

Moorish Idol.
RENÉ L. A. CATALA
PHOTO.

This is a difficult fish to keep in captivity, probably because some element is lacking in its food; a longevity of one year is unusual. It is thought to feed on sponges, or small organisms found in sponges, in nature.

Surgeonfishes
PERCIFORMES: ACANTHURIDAE

"Surgeonfishes" and "Doctorfishes" are general names applied to the one hundred or so species of these fishes, because of the sharp-edged, sharp-pointed spine on the side of the body just in front of the tail. The comparison is obviously to a surgeon's scalpel, but comparison to a switchblade knife might be better, for in some the spine is hinged and lies flat in a groove. Called into play, it flicks out and points forward, and the surgeonfish can inflict a vicious gash in another fish—or a careless fisherman's hand—by sideswiping its victim.

Surgeonfishes range from Massachusetts to Brazil in the western Atlantic and are also found in the Indo-Pacific region. Some species have fixed and permanently erected spines instead of concealed ones. Most are under 20 inches long, and they feed mainly on algae nibbled from dead coral and rocks.

The surgeonfish known as the Blue Tang, about 12 inches long, accidentally reaches New York, but usually ranges southward through the West Indies and is common in Florida inshore waters. The young are bright yellow, but adults are blue. Adults of the Yellow Sailfin Tang have a different color variation in the Pacific: around Hawaii they are yellow, but elsewhere, they are dark brown.

Young Blue Tang

Atlantic Mackerel

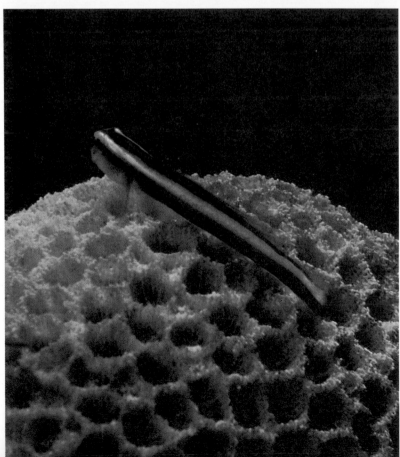

Neon Goby

The Doctorfish, with a bluish blotch around the spine, is the commonest of the surgeonfishes in the Florida-West Indies region. It may stray to Massachusetts and is about 10 inches long.

Mackerels and Tunas
PERCIFORMES: SCOMBRIDAE

An enormous commercial fishing industry centers around the mackerels and tunas of the world's temperate and tropical seas. Throughout the North Atlantic, from Labrador and Norway to Cape Hatteras and Spain, millions of pounds of Atlantic Mackerel are taken each year by trawlers handling nets that may be three miles long. Since mackerels travel in huge schools, the "take" in a single haul of the net can be prodigious.

The Atlantic Mackerel, silvery on the sides and below, dark-barred above, and averaging a foot in length and a pound in weight, has been recorded up to 22 inches and 4 pounds. The schools are found along the Delaware coast in spring, move to Maine as the summer advances, and in the fall drift southward again. They spend the winter well offshore.

Bluefin Tunas are the giants of the family, up to 14 feet and 1,800 pounds, and innumerable accounts have been written of the battles of sport fishermen with large bluefins. In the Pacific the Albacore brings a high price for canning, because of its white meat. The average weight is 40 pounds, the record, 80 pounds.

Gobies
PERCIFORMES: GOBIIDAE

Most of the four hundred or so species of goby live around coral reefs or close inshore, often in tide pools, in the temperate and warm seas of the world, although a few have taken to deep water and even to fresh water. They have a suction area on the

173

forward part of the body, formed by the fusion of the pelvic fins, and this enables them to cling to underwater surfaces and to withstand the battering of waves like those that sweep into tide pools.

See page 172

Small as they are—most are between 2 and 4 inches long—they include some real beauties, such as the 2-inch Neon Goby of the Florida Keys to the southwestern Gulf of Mexico area. Its dark body bears a neon blue stripe on each side.

The smallest fishes in the world are gobies: the Pygmy Goby and the Luzon Goby, both of the Philippines, which are adult at a length of half an inch.

Mudskipper
PERCIFORMES: PERIOPHTHALMIDAE

The popeyed, goby-like little Mudskipper of Africa, Asia, and Australia has been called the most amphibious of all fishes — and indeed it is quite at home on mud flats and among mangrove roots after the tide has receded. Here, a true "fish out of water," it does its feeding on insects and small crustaceans.

Mudskipper

On mud and roots it gets about easily by the fore-and-aft *Zebrafish*
and sideways motions of its large pectoral fins, pulling itself
along as if the fins were crutches. When it needs to make speed,
it can make prodigious hops. In the water it swims normally.

Mudskippers can stay out of water for longer periods than
they spend in it because they carry a mouthful of water in the
gill cavity when they go on land; they also gulp air. This is, of
course, an adaptation to life in an oxygen-depleted environment,
as the water around mud flats and mangrove roots often is. The
Mudskipper must, however, return briefly to water from time to
time to moisten the gills and skin of the body. Its prominent,
protruding eyes can be turned in all directions.

Scorpionfishes and Rockfishes
PERCIFORMES: SCORPAENIDAE

A Zebrafish drifting through the water with all fins spread
inevitably brings to mind a majestic ship in full sail with pen-
nants fluttering. The picture loses some of its romance, however,

when it is realized that eighteen of those striped and spotted spines are venomous. There is no authenticated record of death having been caused by them, but a New York Aquarium tank-man whose finger was punctured by three spines was in severe pain for a day.

There is nothing picturesque about another member of the family, the Stonefish. Not only is it repulsive in appearance, but it is unquestionably the world's most venomous fish, and there is no doubt about human beings dying after stepping on a Stone-fish—a welcome end to almost unbearable pain.

Scorpionfishes and rockfishes—so called because of their venomous spines and their habit of lying on the bottom among rocks—are a fairly large family of several hundred species, found mostly close inshore in cold, temperate, and tropical seas.

The foot-long Zebrafish (or Lionfish, Turkeyfish, or Dragon-fish, to mention a few of its many common names) lives in the shallows of the tropical Indian and western Pacific oceans. Thirteen of its venomous spines are in the fin on the back, and the fish habitually points these toward an enemy, actually making a jabbing attack motion toward an approaching object. Presumably the venom is used only for defense, for the Zebrafish feeds on

Stonefish

crabs, shrimps, and small fishes, which it gulps down in the normal way.

The warty, slime-coated Stonefish also uses its venom for defense, but in a different way. It lies on the bottom, partly buried in sand, and its mottled appearance conceals it in the rocky surface it prefers. The thirteen spines on its back have paired venom sacs at their bases, and anyone unwary enough to step on a Stonefish receives an instant injection of virulent venom. Death may occur within an hour. Fortunately, in recent years government laboratories in Australia have developed an antivenin serum against Stonefish punctures, and it has been found that injected emetine hydrochloride gives dramatically quick relief from the intense pain.

Stonefishes lie in wait for their prey and make a quick forward snap when it approaches. A motion picture made at the New York Aquarium showed that from the opening of the mouth and the snap at approaching food to the return to resting position only one-sixteenth of a second elapsed.

Fireworksfish. From East Africa to Australia and the Philippines. It is about 7¹/₂ inches long and its spines are venomous. (Scorpaenidae).

Searobins

PERCIFORMES: TRIGLIDAE

The big-headed searobins are bottom-dwelling fishes with the interesting habit of "walking" over the bottom by means of the three sensitive rays of each pectoral fin. The rays, separate from the very large pectoral fins, are bent down at the tip and hook into the sand like exploratory fingers. The fishes feed on small crustaceans they encounter.

Searobins are found in warm and temperate seas around the world, chiefly in shallow water. Along the western Atlantic coast the Northern Searobin, 16 inches long and weighing about 1¾ pounds, is fairly common from Cape Cod to northern South America; the slightly larger Striped Searobin of the same general range is often taken in pound nets in the New York area. Both of these fishes are quite good eating, but seldom appear on the market because of a prejudice against them; admittedly, their large bony heads are not very attractive.

Northern Searobin   Probably all searobins are capable of producing noises; cer-

tainly the local ones are. They are particularly noisy at spawning time in midsummer, producing sounds by muscles attached to the gasbladder that cause it to vibrate.

Sculpins
PERCIFORMES: COTTIDAE

Despite the earnest testimony of persons who have tried them, sculpins are not in much demand as a food fish; appearances are against them. In fact, the name "sculpin" has entered the dictionary as a term for "a mean, worthless person."

There are some three hundred species, mostly in cold northern waters along the shores, although some are entirely freshwater species—such as the 4-inch Miller's Thumb of most of Europe. A big, bony head, a body that tapers rapidly backward and may be bare or armed with bony plates and prickles, and eyes high on the head are sculpin characteristics. They are bottom-feeders for the most part, taking crustaceans and small fishes. Most are small.

Longhorn Sculpin

Sea Raven

The Sea Raven of Labrador to Chesapeake Bay is sizable, however: 25 inches and 5 pounds. Its usual color is reddish brown or purplish, but there is a bright yellow color-phase that some fishermen regard superstitiously. Hooked or taken out of the water, the Sea Raven gulps air to inflate itself, somewhat like the puffers. Fishermen use it chiefly for bait.

See page 179

The Longhorn Sculpin is found through about the same range; it reaches a length of 18 inches, spawns in midwinter along the coast, and moves into deep water in the summer.

Europe's little Miller's Thumb of fast-flowing streams seeks out dead shells and the underside of rocks to deposit its eggs; some other European freshwater sculpins turn shells over and form a cavern under them.

Blennies
PERCIFORMES: BLENNIIDAE

There are about a dozen families of blenny-like fishes in the world's seas, mostly living on the bottom in shallow water and feeding on other fishes or taking nearly anything that comes their way. Those in this family are scaleless and tropical, and

many have peculiar head accessories, such as crests and fringes. The Fringehead Blenny of the Mediterranean, for example, has a fleshy little "tree" growing on its forehead.

Klipfishes
PERCIFORMES: CLINIDAE

Ritual fighting is indulged in by the males of some of the klipfishes, and the rules are just as fixed as they are for prize-fighting. Two males may meet face to face or side by side, with mouth open and gill covers raised, and seek to intimidate each other. The Bluethroat Pikeblennies of Florida waters are especially pugnacious, and when one male invades the territory of another, the ritualization of their display may well end with one biting the other and driving him off.

Eelpouts
PERCIFORMES: ZOARCIDAE

Food-fish fashions change, and a good example is the Ocean Pout. Large numbers are caught in commercial fishing operations in cold North Atlantic waters, and for a long time they were routinely dumped overboard as "trash fishes"—for admittedly, the 3-foot-long, eellike, dark fish is not very appetizing in appearance. But the flesh under the dark skin is quite edible, and now Ocean Pouts are just as routinely saved and brought to market.

Ocean Pout

There are some sixty species of eelpout, most of them not much more than a foot long, and they live in the cold seas of both the Northern and Southern hemispheres, from the shallows to depths of more than a mile.

Pearlfishes
PERCIFORMES: CARAPIDAE

"Pearlfish" is a general name for perhaps two dozen small, eellike fishes of usually shallow marine waters all over the world that live inside pearl shells, clams, starfish, sea cucumbers, and a few other marine invertebrates; they are equally well called Sea Cucumber Fishes, and one species from Florida and the West Indies almost exclusively haunts a single species of Sea Cucumber, *Actinopyga agassizi*, of those waters. Other fishes may be rapidly killed by a poison given off by the Sea Cucumber when it expels its internal organs as a defensive measure, but the Pearlfish is unharmed except when there is a heavy concentration of the poisonous substance in a confined space.

A Pearlfish enters the Sea Cucumber's body through the vent, entering headfirst in the beginning, but later going in tailfirst with a corkscrew motion. It may feed on the internal organs—without triggering evisceration—or feed outside and re-enter the Sea Cucumber for protection. Most Pearlfishes are less than 6 inches long.

Butterfishes
PERCIFORMES: STROMATEIDAE

Butterfishes are a valuable food fish, and great numbers are taken in pound nets along the Atlantic coast from Maine to North Carolina. They also provide good sport for amateur fishermen working from the wharves and along pilings. Twelve inches is about the maximum size.

Young Butterfishes have the interesting habit of taking shelter under floating jellyfishes.

Shepherdfishes
PERCIFORMES: NOMEIDAE

The rather fanciful name of shepherdfish has been given to certain small nomeids that trail around with such huge jelly-fishes as the Portuguese Man-of-War—not, it is true, "sheep-herding" their protectors, but rather being in the position of helpless sheep in the care of a huge and benevolent wolf. The Man-of-War Fish is only about 3 inches long, and it lives un-harmed among the stinging tentacles of the jellyfish. It is found throughout tropical seas.

Gouramis, Fighting Fishes, Climbing Perch
PERCIFORMES: ANABANTIDAE

Many fishes do things that seem strange to us—however natural to them—but not many are as celebrated as those that kiss, fight, and climb (or, more usually, walk on land). The Kiss-ing Gourami, the Siamese Fighting Fish, and the Climbing

Climbing Perch

183

Perch are small freshwater tropicals of southeast Asia and Africa that are often kept by home aquarium fanciers.

The mainly white, 10-inch Kissing Gourami of the Malay Peninsula, Thailand, and the Sunda Islands has a protrusible, suckerlike mouth. On occasion—what sets them off is not certainly known—two fish will place their lips in contact and remain in that position for as long as twenty-five minutes. There has been much speculation as to whether this act is courtship, mouth cleaning, or aggression.

Many fish fight each other, but combat is usually short and bloodless—the less aggressive fish turns tail and flees. Not so with the males of the Siamese Fighting Fish; they will slug it out until exhaustion or injuries stop the fight. In their native waters they are quite unimpressive 2-inch little creatures, but their fighting propensities have long been recognized, and selective breeding for endurance and pugnacity has produced bettas with the tenacity of bulldogs. Fights between bettas are a recognized sport in Thailand.

Other domesticated strains have been selectively bred for color and large fins. These are the brilliantly colored males with veillike fins found in pet stores. They are still fighters, however, and it is a good idea to keep males separated by sheets of glass.

See page 183

The common name of the Climbing Perch is misleading; it is not a true perch, and while it does climb a few inches up a conveniently sloping tree trunk on occasion, this is incidental to its wandering on land, either in the dewy morning or during rainstorms, from one body of water to another. Whole troupes of fish travel in this way, rocking and wriggling along with their extended gill covers as props. They can cover 10 feet in a minute.

The Climbing Perch is about 10 inches long, lives in southeastern Asia, and except for its walking habits is undistinguished —just a little gray-brown fish.

Kissing Gourami in kissing posture

Great Barracuda

Barracudas
PERCIFORMES: SPHYRAENIDAE

In any list of the half-dozen most dangerous fishes in the world, the Great Barracuda of the tropical Atlantic and the western Pacific is sure to be included. Not that it attacks invariably and on sight; divers know well its habit of circling around them, stalking them as it were—and more often than not eventually drifting away. On the other hand, when one does attack, it can bite off a great piece of flesh with its razor-sharp teeth concealed in the large mouth. A barracuda's bite is clean, quite unlike that of the sharks, and is readily distinguished. In earlier days many barracuda bites were probably attributed to sharks.

The Great Barracuda reaches a length of 6 feet, sometimes more. Its normal food is other fishes, which it may herd into a tight, frightened school before making an attack.

In the North Atlantic the 12-inch Northern Barracuda is sometimes taken in New York Harbor.

Mullets
PERCIFORMES: MUGILIDAE

Despite the fact that they are bottom-grubbing fishes, mullets are important food fishes and are caught commercially. There are about one hundred species, in shallow waters of the tropical and temperate seas all over the world. The Striped Mullet ranges from Massachusetts to Brazil, and since it reaches a length of about 3 feet, may weigh 15 pounds, and moves in large schools, it is caught in great numbers wherever it happens to be abundant. The White Mullet of about the same range is considerably smaller, but is also a good food fish.

Mullets are generally known as Gray Mullets in Europe. In an aquarium they have been observed swimming in dense schools by day, but going to rest on the bottom at night and "bedding down" facing in different directions.

Grunions spawning on a California beach. Donald W. Wilkie Photo — T. Wayland Vaughan Aquarium.

Silversides
PERCIFORMES: ATHERINIDAE

Silversides are abundant, glittering little fishes of some 150 species, mostly of tropical and temperate marine waters around the world, but with some in fresh and brackish waters. One of the most celebrated is the Grunion, which spawns on the beaches of southern and Lower California at the time of the highest tides. Millions wriggle onto the wet sand, bury their eggs at a depth of about 2 inches, and then attempt to flop back into the water before the local people can scoop them up by the bucketful. They are excellent eating. Two weeks later the eggs hatch within minutes at the next extra-high tide.

Large numbers of Silversides, also called Spearing, are seined in shallow water along the North Atlantic ocean beaches and are used as bait. Young of the Tidewater Silversides are the so-called whitebait of the fish markets.

Left-eye Flounders
PERCIFORMES: BOTHIDAE

Flounders and soles, although in three families, are all flat-fishes, which characteristically lie flat on the ocean floor. They start life by swimming in the normal fashion, one eye on either side of the head, but with growth one eye gradually moves over the top of the skull to lie close to the other eye on top of the head, and the fish assumes a flat, reclining position. Generally the underside is white.

The left-eye flounders of the Atlantic and Pacific are both shallow water and deep-water fishes, and some divide the seasons between the shallows and deeps. Along the Atlantic coast from Cape Cod to South Carolina the Summer Flounder (sometimes called the Fluke in the New York area) is an excellent food fish that is commonly taken by anglers and commercial fishermen in summer; it disappears with the coming of cold weather and moves offshore to deep water. A usual size is about 5 pounds, but it has reached 26 pounds and 46 inches.

Right-eye Flounders
PERCIFORMES: PLEURONECTIDAE

The huge Atlantic Halibut and the Winter Flounder are well-known representatives of this family along the North Atlantic shores. Their development is typically like that of the flatfishes.

The Atlantic Halibut occurs around the world in northern seas and ranges south in the Atlantic to New Jersey and the Bay of Biscay. The record for size is 9 feet and 700 pounds, but they seldom exceed 450 pounds. This is an important fish to the commercial fishing industry—as is the related Pacific Halibut that attains a weight of 470 pounds. Halibut are prolific—a 200-pound female can produce more than two million eggs—and are voracious feeders as they roam the seas in packs.

Winter Flounders, common in Long Island waters, have a range from Labrador to Georgia and are found mostly on sandy or muddy bottoms to a depth of 120 feet or more. They feed for the most part on crustaceans and mollusks, sometimes on small fishes, and only rarely reach 15 inches and a weight of 1½ pounds.

Winter Flounder

*Sharksuckers,
or Remoras, attached
to the glass front
of a tank*

Soles
PERCIFORMES: SOLEIDAE

Despite the fact that true soles are found along the western Atlantic coast, the "fillet of sole" served in American restaurants is likely to be fillet of Winter Flounder or some other flounder; the commonest true sole of our waters rejoices in the name of Hogchoker and is not eaten. The original and actual fillet of sole comes from the European Sole.

The Hogchoker ranges from Cape Ann to the Gulf of Mexico, generally on sandy or muddy bottoms, and the young especially may move into brackish or fresh water. Both eyes are on the right side of the head, and the Hogchoker can be readily identified by its flatfish form, transverse lines across the eyed side, and dark spots on the blind side—markings not found on any other soles. It is about 6 inches long.

Remoras, or Suckerfishes
ORDER ECHENEIFORMES: ECHENEIDAE

Remoras, or suckerfishes, are the hitchhikers of the seas, not bothering to thumb a ride, but attaching themselves to bigger fish, especially sharks, and hanging on by means of a powerful suction disk on the top of the head. There are only a few species, but they are found all through the tropical and temperate seas and are recorded as attached not only to sharks but to turtles, porpoises, marlin, whales, and ships.

It has long been supposed that they feed on bits of food scattered by their hosts, but at least some are now known to eat parasites on the body of the hosts.

Their suction power is remarkable. A sizable specimen of the Sharksucker, which is found along the Atlantic coast to Massachusetts, was tested in the New York Aquarium, and when it was held by the tail and lifted, it bore the weight of a 28-pound pail of water. It is sometimes used by African natives and others to catch fish and turtles; released with a line tied around its tail, it is more certain than a fishhook. The Sharksucker is the largest of the remoras, about 36 inches long. The smallest species is 7 inches long.

Triggerfishes and Filefishes
ORDER TETRAODONTIFORMES: BALISTIDAE

A defensive spine that can be erected at will and then locked into place so that it will break before it can be forcibly depressed is a peculiarity of the triggerfishes. This mechanism

Queen Triggerfish
Clown Triggerfish

Humuhumu-nukunuku-a-puaa

is in the dorsal fin. The first fin spine is very long and hollowed out behind; when it is erected, a bony knob at the base of the second spine moves into the hollow and holds the first spine rigidly upright. An enemy adroit enough to get at the "trigger" spine could release the lock, but it would have to be dexterous indeed to overcome a triggerfish locked into a coral head.

Triggerfishes and filefishes are compressed, small-mouthed, rather leathery-skinned fishes primarily of shallow tropical seas, although some do wander into temperate waters. Many are beautifully marked, such as the brilliant 15-inch Queen Triggerfish *See page 189* of both sides of the tropical Atlantic and the Indian Ocean, with its vivid blue lines and streaks, and the boldly spotted, orange-lipped Clown Triggerfish of the tropical Indo-Pacific. The Queen *See page 189* is common around Florida and strays to Massachusetts. The Gray Triggerfish is a slightly smaller species that drifts northward in the Gulf Stream in late summer and autumn and is occasionally caught in New England waters.

One triggerfish of the tropical Indo-Pacific is interesting to Aquarium visitors for two good reasons. One is its color and pattern of soft mauve, light blue, white, and rich brown, and the other is its Hawaiian name: Humuhumu-nukunuku-a-puaa (pronounced just as it is spelled!).

The essentially tropical filefishes are so called because of the texture of their hard, rough skin. At one time it was commonplace for fishing smacks to have a strip of dried filefish skin tacked up beside the galley stove for scratching matches.

Largest of the filefishes is the 3-foot Scrawled Filefish, prettily marked with broken blue lines and dots. It has a rather slender, tapering body, and small ones have been reported taking a head-down position in eelgrass in the Bermuda region, apparently as a sort of camouflage. It may wander as far north as New York, but the Planehead Filefish, about 10 inches long, has often been recorded all the way to Maine. Its color is highly variable, from slaty gray to bright green.

Filefishes lack the trigger mechanism of the triggerfishes and instead of three dorsal spines have only one.

Gray Triggerfish

Trunkfishes
TETRAODONTIFORMES: OSTRACIIDAE

"Tortoises of the sea" is an apt description of the trunk-fishes, for they are encased in a bony box composed of fused scales. Rigid and incapable of sinuous body movements, they propel themselves slowly by means of the fins, and when in a hurry, by sculling motions of the tail. Speed would never enable them to escape active predators, but a hard box is certainly not very palatable to other fishes.

On the other hand, it *is* convenient to people in the West Indies and the Indo-Pacific who like a ready-made "covered dish" meal—they simply roast or bake the fish in its shell.

The grotesque, triangular-bodied Cowfishes of both sides of the tropical Atlantic are handsomely marked with reticulations; indeed, some of the Indo-Pacific trunkfishes are strikingly beautiful. The range of adult Scrawled Cowfishes in the western Atlantic is from the Carolinas to Brazil, but juveniles, about half an inch long, are sometimes carried as far north as Massachusetts by the Gulf Stream. The name "Cowfish," incidentally, comes from the spines, or "horns," that project from the top of the head and above the eyes. The Cowfish grows to 18 inches or a little longer.

Baby Trunkfishes about 1 inch long are occasionally seen along the New York coast, drifters from Florida waters. The adults, about 9 inches long, are olive gray, and most scales bear a faint blue spot.

The Smooth Trunkfish ranging from the North Atlantic into the West Indies is one of several trunkfishes that release a mucus poison that can kill other fishes in a closed water system or in close contact.

Scrawled Cowfish

Puffers

TETRAODONTIFORMES: TETRAODONTIDAE

"Puffer," "Swellfish," "Blowfish"—all these common names well describe a family of fishes with the ability to gulp air or water until their bodies are almost spherical. Presumably this is an effective underwater defense against the attacks of predators, which find it difficult to take a bite out of a water-filled balloon. Puffers become inflated with air, of course, only when they are hauled out of the water. Then, in a few seconds and with convulsive gulps they swell until not much more than the stubby tail projects from the body. Thrown back in the water, they float until they become deflated and then swim away.

The Northern Puffer breeds along the coast north to New

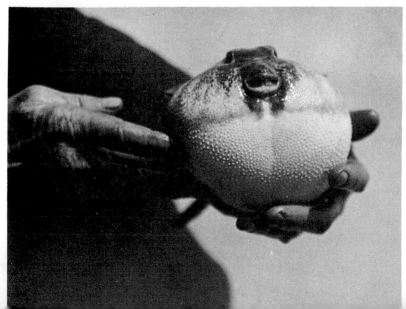

Northern Puffer, Swellfish or Blowfish. LEFT: *The same fish inflated with air.*

York and is often caught off piers and breakwaters around Cape Cod. Adults reach a length of about 10 inches. Baby Northern Puffers have been captured when they are no more than one-fourth of an inch long, by which time they, too, are able to swell up into little morsels about the size of a pea.

Puffers have a bad reputation for poisoning people who eat their flesh; and while puffers are much enjoyed in Japan, those who cook them must be specially trained and licensed. Along the Atlantic coast they were long ignored as food, until it was discovered that the fleshy stalk of the tail of the Northern Puffer was harmless and very good eating indeed. It is often called "Sea Squab" on bills of fare.

Porcupinefishes
TETRAODONTIFORMES: DIODONTIDAE

Probably the worst enemy of the Porcupinefish is man—who eviscerates it, dries its distended skin, fixes a light bulb inside, and sells it to tourists in the tropics. Certainly few predatory fishes would care to make a mouthful of a Porcupinefish when it swells to a sphere, like the puffers, but with the addition of a thick body-covering and very sharp spines.

Oyster Toadfishes sheltered in bottom debris

There are some fifteen species of porcupinefish in the warm seas of the world. The Porcupinefish of all temperate and tropical oceans is the largest member of the family, up to 3 feet long. It is most at home in the warmer waters as far as northern Florida, but is occasionally seen off Massachusetts as a Gulf Stream drifter in summer. Its spines are in their best defensive posture when the Porcupinefish gulps water and swells to an almost perfect sphere.

The much smaller Spiny Boxfish, not so prompt to inflate itself as the Porcupinefish, is a late-summer visitor around New York and slightly northward. *See page 196*

Toadfishes
ORDER BATRACHOIDIFORMES: BATRACHOIDIDAE

Many years ago the New York Aquarium acquired half a dozen Toadfishes and put them on temporary exhibition in a nice, clean, sandy-bottomed, and otherwise barren tank. Visibility was perfect — if the visitor could manage to distinguish one Toadfish from another; they all clumped together, one on top of another, in a quivering mass "looking like an aggregation of overgrown tadpoles."

What they wanted was obvious, and so the Aquarium staff raided a garbage pile, collected rusty tin cans, broken bottles, and a pair of discarded shoes, and dumped them into the Toadfish tank. Within minutes each Toadfish had found just the "house" it was looking for and had moved in. There were not quite enough houses, but even the homeless Toadfishes were content when they snuggled up beside an old shoe or under a can.

Toadfishes have been called repulsive because of their broad, flat head, rapidly tapering body, and dark blotches. There are about thirty species in temperate and tropical seas, and the Oyster Toadfish, 10 to 12 inches long, occurs close inshore from Maine to Cuba. Man is a blessing to the Toadfish; he dumps all kinds of junk into the water and thus provides them with homes. Crustaceans, small fishes, and mollusks are the usual food taken as the Toadfish cruises the bottom, but it does not disdain edible garbage.

It is pugnacious, too, especially in the breeding season, and will snap at anything that approaches; a Toadfish can be lifted out of the water when it closes its strong jaws on a stick. Eggs are generally deposited in the kind of receptacle that serves as a Toadfish home, or else in empty shells or on sunken boards or the like, and are guarded by the male.

Spiny Boxfish

Toadfishes produce sounds by vibration of the gasbladder, variously described as growls, grunts, and whistles.

One of them, the Northern Midshipman of South Carolina to the Gulf and down to Argentina, is so noisy that in some places it is called the "Singing Fish." It is about 8 inches long.

Anglers
ORDER LOPHIIFORMES: LOPHIIDAE

Just above the sandy bottom a small, wormlike object is twitching and waving. A small fish approaches: obviously, here is a tasty snack. The next instant the small fish has disappeared; it has itself become a snack for a waiting angler buried in the sand and waving its "bait" of flabby tissue at the end of the fishing-pole spine projecting above its enormous mouth.

The Goosefish of the western Atlantic, from the Gulf of St. Lawrence to Cape Hatteras, is among two-hundred-some-odd species of anglerfish in this order throughout the temperate and tropical seas. It is big and repulsive, some 4 feet long and up to

45 pounds in weight—there is one record of 70 pounds. The most obvious thing about it, apart from the waving lure, is the mouth, which is almost as wide as the whole body. Flaps of skin fringe the lower jaw and most of the body.

Goosefishes have voracious appetites, and while they feed mostly on fishes and crabs, they take anything they can get, including diving sea birds.

Their eggs are deposited in sticky bands that may be 40 feet long and 2 feet wide.

Frogfishes
LOPHIIFORMES: ANTENNARIIDAE

Splitlure Frogfish with its "fishing pole" extended

One of the most interesting of the small frogfishes, part of the group that uses dangling lures to attract prey, is the Sargassumfish of the tropical Atlantic, which occasionally straggles north to Cape Cod. It is almost invariably found clinging to a drifting clump of Sargassum weed, which it so much resembles in broken outline and dark stripes and mottled patches that it is not easy to see. It is seldom more than 6 inches long and is so well adapted to its Sargassum-weed home that it can slowly change color to match its surroundings and can actually climb through the weed by clasping with its pectoral fins.

Even more "feathery" because of the filaments of skin on its body is the Splitlure Frogfish of the Atlantic coast, from New Jersey to Brazil. Instead of a single lure at the end of its "fishing pole," the large, light-colored tab is divided.

See page 197

Sargassumfish in seaweed

Splitlure Frogfish. WOMETCO MIAMI SEAQUARIUM PHOTO.

Frogfish of the warm seas from East Africa to Hawaii. It is found around coral and sponges. RENÉ L. A. CATALA PHOTO.

INVERTEBRATES

Most of the animals that live in water are invertebrates; that is, they have no backbone. In fact, all animal life, whether on land or in the air or in water, can be split into two very unequal parts: the backboned animals (some 41,200 species) and the backboneless (perhaps a million species, with more being described and named every year).

The water-dwelling invertebrates exist in every degree of complexity, from one-celled organisms that can be seen only under a microscope to squids 50 feet long. Some are known only to professional zoologists (who do not always agree in classifying them), and others are familiar to all of us — we can go into any seafood shop and pick out clams, oysters, crabs, shrimps, and lobsters. These happen to be invertebrates that have a hard or stiffening cover to their bodies — a shell — but equally typical are the soft and watery jellyfishes and the flabby sea anemones. Lack of a backbone does not necessarily mean lack of a skeleton; since ancient times men have used the skeletons of certain sponges for wiping up spilled liquids or bathing, and pretty pieces of coral and sea fans — skeletons — decorate many a mantelpiece.

Invertebrates live in both salt and fresh water, and many of the most colorful flourish in the cold and temperate seas. All are cold-blooded; that is, they take their temperature from that of the water surrounding them, be it the perpetual cold of the ocean depths (invertebrates have been dredged up from 30,000 feet off the Philippines) or warm springs around 133° F. Some can move and do so constantly, by means of whiplike processes, bodily pulsations, forcible ejection of water, or the slow movement of "feet." Many are mobile in early stages and then settle down to one spot for the rest of their lives — which may be surprisingly long. One sea anemone was kept in "captivity" for about eighty years.

Most of us have to stir about to earn a living and get food; not so the sedentary invertebrates. Water that carries food is always in motion, or can be put in motion by the animal's own action, such as whipping water into the mouth by means of minute cilia. Sometimes the food comes of its own accord, inadvertently, as when a fish blunders into the tentacles of a sea anemone and is trapped.

By and large the invertebrates of the water world are harmless as far as man is concerned, with exceptions such as the Portuguese Man-of-War whose stinging cells carried on long, trailing tentacles can raise inflamed welts and cause cramps or death in a swimmer, or the "venomous" Elkhorn Coral of the West Indies. Australian bathers would probably put the deadly sea wasps at the head of the list. In the West Indies sea urchins are a real hazard, for their spines may be a foot long, and anyone stepping on such a pincushion is sure to regret it.

Comparatively few of the thousands of species of water-dwelling invertebrates can be exhibited, even in the largest Aquarium. Even fewer touch our lives economically. But anyone who has explored a living coral reef or a garden of sea anemones or admired the liquid flow of an octopus must admit their aesthetic appeal.

The classification of invertebrates in the section that follows is based on, but does not always follow, "Zoological Names: A List of Phyla, Classes and Orders" prepared for the American Association for the Advancement of Science (1948).

One-celled Animals
PHYLUM PROTOZOA

The animal-plant food chain of life has to start somewhere, and on the animal side it starts here, with the one-celled, microscopic protozoans, or "first animals." (The plant side of the chain starts with similarly one-celled protophytans, or "first plants").

There are protozoans in every tank in every aquarium, but unless a special microscopic exhibit has been set up, they are never seen — they are too small. The only reason for mentioning them here is that they are an essential part of the food base in natural waters and that some of them are annoying, dangerous, or sometimes fatal parasites of fishes. Anyone who has seen the effects of the "red tide" — an outbreak, or "blooming," of the protozoans known as dinoflagellates — will realize how enormously destructive they can be to marine fishes under certain conditions.

On the other hand, they do add a dramatic touch to the seascape. Billions of pinhead-sized dinoflagellates called Noctiluca ("Night light") tint the surface of the sea pink by day and paint the crests of breaking waves with a cold, eerie luminescence after dark. Ships ploughing through the world's oceans trail a moonlight path of luminescence behind them as propellers churn the water. Noctiluca, of course, is only one of many marine organisms possessing luminescence.

A marine plankton haul composed mostly of dinoflagellates

The Sponges

PHYLUM PORIFERA: CLASS DEMOSPONGIAE

Although there are some 4,500 species of sponge in the seas of the world (plus about 150 species of freshwater sponge in a single family), most of us are likely to know only the few commercial sponges that are used in the bathroom, in industry, and for washing automobiles. They are members of the large Class Demospongiae to which four-fifths of the sponges belong.

Actually we know only the horny skeletons of those sponges, for the living animals are quite different in appearance —dark, leathery, flabby, "spongy" balls or chunks of living matter hauled up from the bottom of the shallow seas. When the sponge dies and decomposes, the tissue can be washed away.

A century or so ago sponges were thought to be plants, or perhaps plant-animals, or even some mysterious natural secretion. Like a plant, they are fixed for life in one spot on the bottom, or on rocks, pilings, or other places. Like some plants, too, they can be propagated by cuttings — snip off a piece, give it a place to rest and attach itself, and in time it becomes another sponge.

A good deal more is known about sponges now. The living body is covered with countless pores. Water is drawn into internal canals through these pores and is then released through larger openings after the nutrients are extracted — protozoans and microscopic algae, minute eggs and organic debris. Reproduction may be by "budding," in which cells grow out from the side of the body, pinch off at the base, and drop to start a new sponge, or by the casting off of spores that form new sponges. The method of taking a "cutting" and planting it elsewhere is practiced by

Red Beard Sponge

sponge fishermen to increase the commercial take — which, incidentally, is woefully reduced in Florida and Caribbean waters since the outbreak of a fungus disease in the 1930's.

Sponges are found in every sea, from the shallows to ocean depths of 21,000 feet, from the tropics to the polar seas. Some are so small that dozens would fit on a penny, others are giants 5 or 6 feet tall. It is no wonder early zoologists were confused by the sponges, for they vary enormously in color, shape, and size, all within the same species. They may be red, yellow, green, blue, black, white, violet, or any tint in between; they may be cup-shaped, vase-shaped, branched or domed or fanlike, big or little — and all the same species! Form, color, and size depend upon the circumstances of their habitat, and the only sure (or reasonably sure) way of identifying wildly varying specimens is by the structure of their skeletal spicules.

Strollers on the seashore often encounter clamshells perforated by hundreds of small holes. These are the work of the Boring Sponge, abundant from Cape Cod to South Carolina and very destructive to clams and oysters.

The New York Aquarium has a sponge exhibit that came of its own accord — large numbers of the small white Glove Sponge and the Red Beard Sponge that entered the tanks probably through sea water when captured fish were being dumped into the tanks or perhaps on rocks or other tank decorations brought from the sea. The Red Beard Sponge is commonly found on oyster and scallop shells in Long Island Sound and may grow to a branched form up to 10 inches high.

Hydroids, Jellyfishes, Sea Anemones, and Corals

PHYLUM CNIDARIA

"Flowers of the sea" is a trite but useful description of the cnidarians — except, of course, that they are carnivorous animals instead of plants. Certainly any terrestrial gardener would be happy to match a "sea garden" of cnidarians with their almost psychedelic opulence of color and form.

There are some nine thousand species, in all seas from the tropical shallows to the polar oceans, plus a few small freshwater hydras and jellyfishes. The general characteristics of the cnidarians are radial symmetry and an array of stinging tentacles by which food is captured and drawn into the central mouth. Many are permanently attached to their home site, but others, such as the jellyfishes, are free-swimming. In addition to their normal colors, many are luminescent when disturbed by contact.

Hydrozoans and Jellyfishes
CNIDARIA: CLASS HYDROZOA

The "stings" of cnidarians are tiny barbs attached to threads coiled in capsules in the animals' tentacles. They are discharged by contact with the tentacles, and some are specialized to discharge a venom. Other threads are adhesive or wrap around the victim like a lasso. These devices are quite effective against small fishes, which may be killed or paralyzed, and those of the Stinging Coral of the Caribbean region can make even a tough-handed skin diver wish he had not brushed against the pretty pink branches. The hydrocorals of tropical and temperate seas secrete heavy limestone skeletons and often form a part of coral reefs.

The most dangerous of the hydrozoans is undoubtedly the famous — or infamous — Portuguese Man-of-War of the Atlantic, Pacific, and Indian oceans. It is large, up to 14 inches along the gas-filled float that rides the surface of the warm seas, and is indeed quite pretty, for the float flashes with iridescent blue,

Portuguese Men-of-War cast up on the beach. WOMETCO MIAMI SEAQUARIUM PHOTO.

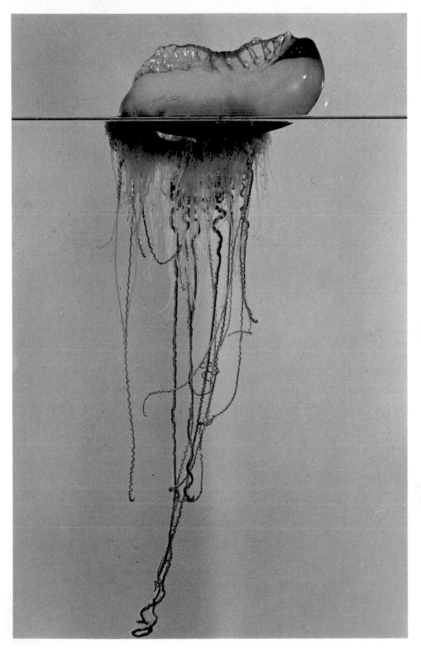

Portuguese Man-of-War. CHARLES E. LANE PHOTO, UNIVERSITY OF MIAMI.

green, or red. The "business end" of the animal, however, is out of sight: scores of tentacles that may trail as much as 100 feet below and behind the float as it drifts. They can deliver a paralyzing sting to anything—even a man—that comes in contact with them, although there are no instances of human beings actually dying from severe contacts. Oddly enough, a small fish has gained the name of Portuguese-Man-of-War Fish by living

Cassiopeia, or Upside-down Jellyfish

unharmed among the stinging tentacles. Whether it has acquired an immunity is not definitely known; in any event, it has a safe shelter and may be useful to the Man-of-War by attracting predators into the tentacles.

A number of other floating hydrozoans are more or less like the Portuguese Man-of-War in their structure and habits, including the "By-the-Wind Sailor," which is 1 to 3 inches long, with a blue or purple body suspended from the gas-filled float. Vast numbers are sometimes washed up on the shores of Florida or the west coast of America. Its sting is not dangerous to man. These floating animals are essentially tropical, but they float at the mercy of the winds, hence their occurrence on North American and European shores.

"By-the-Wind Sailor."
ALICE S. KESLER
PHOTO.

True Jellyfishes
CNIDARIA: CLASS SCYPHOZOA

Jellyfishes are umbrella-shaped animals that are at least 94 per cent water. Sense organs and tentacles armed with stinging cells are arranged around the outer edge of the umbrella, and the mouth and stomach are in the center of the lower side. Moving with rhythmic pulsations like the slow opening and closing of an umbrella, they trail their almost invisible armament, and any small fish that brushes against the tentacles is paralyzed and carried to the mouth, engulfed in the stomach, and digested in hours or days.

Largest of the jellyfishes is the Giant Jellyfish of Arctic waters, which occasionally may be 8 feet across the umbrella

See page 208

Noumea Jellyfish. RENÉ
L. A. CATALA PHOTO.

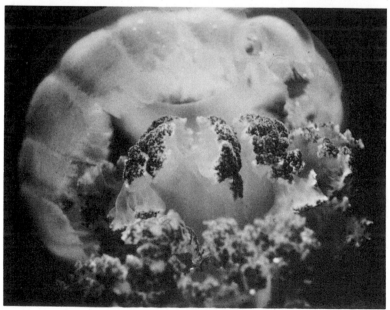

Giant Jellyfish.
CARLETON RAY PHOTO.

and trail some eight hundred tentacles for 200 feet. Such a creature is highly dangerous, and small ones 1 to 3 feet in diameter—those of the size often washed up on the shores of New England—should be respected, even after death, for their "stings" are still effective, and contact with their tentacles is like grasping a stinging nettle.

Large jellyfishes require a comparatively enormous amount of tank room and thus cannot be successfully exhibited, but small specimens a few inches in diameter are often shown. However, they usually end up huddled in the corner of a tank. A common species along the southern shores of New England to the tropics is the Sea Nettle; its 8-inch umbrella carries forty golden tentacles.

Passengers on ships are likely to see the Moon Jellyfish, a white, tough-jellied creature 6 to 10 inches in diameter, often occurring in very large patches. It, too, is often cast up on the shores of the western Atlantic.

Sea wasps have already been mentioned as dangerous. The small, four-sided Pacific Sea Wasps of Australia and the South Pacific have caused the deaths of human beings in anything from thirty seconds to two or three hours. The Sea Wasp occurring erratically from North Carolina to Brazil is less dangerous. Even so, it is well to avoid four-sided, cuboid jellyfishes wherever they are found.

One jellyfish that does quite well in the Aquarium is the Cassiopeia, generally seen resting on the bottom of the tank. It is *See page 206* one of the "many-mouthed" jellyfishes—which simply means that it has many mouths instead of the usual single one. Cassiopeias are common in shallow waters and mangrove bays from Bermuda and Florida to the tropics, and hundreds of them are likely to be seen crowded close together as they feed. From the position it habitually assumes, it is often called the "Upside-down Jellyfish."

Sea Whips, Sea Fans, Sea Anemones, and Corals
CNIDARIA: CLASS ANTHOZOA

The underwater movies of Jacques-Yves Cousteau and other photographers have given the most sedentary of us some idea of the bizarre forms and exuberant colors of a tropical coral reef. Here in almost incomprehensible profusion are the anthozoans, the well-named "flower animals" of the sea. Two-thirds of all the cnidarians are in this group, all of them living in the sea, for the most part in shallow waters along the shores of the tropical and temperate oceans. They are basically cylindrical in form; some are solitary, but many—such as the corals—are colonial and form immense congregations of individual polyps.

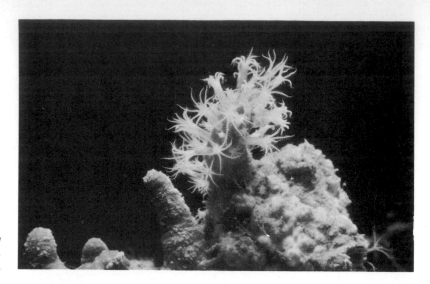

Soft Corals

Soft corals lack the hard lime secretion that forms the skeleton of the stony corals; instead they are stiffened by scattered spicules. One species often takes the form of a hand and in England is called "Dead Men's Fingers." It may actually be flesh-colored — or white or orange — and the "fingers" are covered with transparent whitish polyps.

Soft corals are found in all oceans, sometimes to great depths. In the cooler waters of the North Atlantic there are many species from Delaware northward, in shades of red, salmon, yellow, and purple, some resembling little clusters of mushrooms and others like miniature trees a few inches high.

Sea Whips, Sea Fans

The dried, horny skeletons of sea whips and sea fans are familiar souvenirs of holidays in the subtropics. These are flexible corals that in life look almost plantlike as they bend and sway in the currents. They add much to the beauty of the underwater "forest," for they may be brilliantly red, yellow, orange, or purple. The greatest profusion of sea whips is found in the tropical Indo-Pacific, but sea fans and sea whips are lovely decorations in the shallow waters around Florida, through the Caribbean, and in the Mediterranean, too.

They are occasionally exhibited alive in the New York Aquarium, and the skeletons are often used for tank decorations — especially as convenient "hitching posts" for seahorses.

The beautiful Red, or Precious, Coral from which necklaces are made belongs to this group. It has been harvested for centuries, especially in the Mediterranean. In life, the hard red core is covered with white polyps like fringed blossoms.

OPPOSITE: *Skeleton of a Sea Fan.* WOMETCO MIAMI SEAQUARIUM PHOTO.

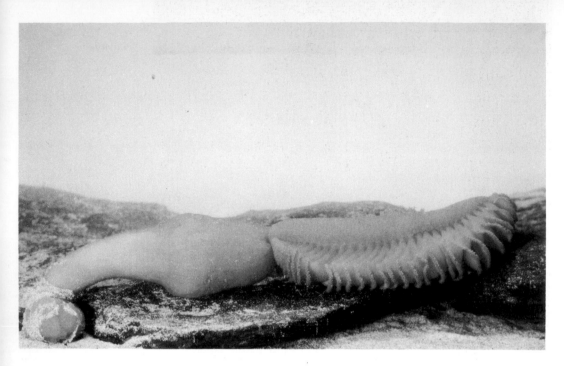

Orange Sea Pen

Sea Pens

Sea pens take their name from their resemblance to the quill pens of olden days, for the cylindrical stalk is crowned with featherlike polyps. They live on soft bottoms in most warm and temperate waters and are colorful additions to the underwater garden, luxuriating in all shades of red and yellow, orange, green, brown, and purple. They are highly luminescent, and when brushed or disturbed, they "blush" with a blue, violet, green, or yellow light. The 2-foot Orange Sea Pen of the American Pacific coast is the species usually exhibited.

Tube Anemones

Tube anemones live inside slender, stiff tubes formed by body secretions in which sand grains are often embedded. The tube is usually buried in the sandy bottom of shallow coastal waters of the temperate Atlantic and Pacific, with little more than the rayed terminal tentacles projecting. When they are disturbed, the tentacles quickly disappear into the top of the tube. The common American Tube Anemone, or Cerianthus, is brown, about 6 inches long, and occurs from Cape Cod to Florida.

Sea Anemones

Anyone who has examined tide pools and rocky shores at low water is likely to be familiar with many kinds of sea anemones, for they are as eye-catching in cold and temperate waters

American Tube Anemone

Brown Sea Anemone

213

as they are in the tropics—red, green, blue, yellow, orange, white, almost any color. All have the same general form: a columnar body surmounted by "petals," which are really the stinging and feeding tentacles that capture tiny free-swimming organisms, occasionally small fishes, crabs, and the like to be stuffed into the mouth in the center of the disk. The tentacles may be comparatively short and stubby, or more threadlike, or even like plumes. They are fully extended when the animal is feeding, but when the sea anemone is disturbed, they are pulled into the body, and the body itself contracts.

One of the larger anemones of the tropical Indo-Pacific is the Yellow-tipped Sea Anemone that provides a home and shelter for the Clownfish; the fish lives unharmed among the stinging tentacles even when the anemone contracts.

See page 213 A small Brown Sea Anemone is common along North Atlantic shores and grows wild in the New York Aquarium's tanks. Equally common is the Powderpuff Anemone and its relative of the Pacific Northwest, the White-plumed Sea Anemone. They belong to a group of beautifully plumed anemones found around the world in northern waters, often hanging from rocks and pilings anywhere from just below the low-tide level to very deep water. Even more striking is the Dahlia Sea Anemone of the deeper waters of the northern oceans, whose stalk is scarlet mottled with green. Its regularly arranged red tentacles are sometimes banded with white.

Dahlia Sea Anemone

Powderpuff Sea Anemone of the American Pacific coast

The White-armed Sea Anemone, found from Cape Cod to North Carolina, is plentiful in Long Island Sound. Like other anemones, it can move by slow extensions of its attachment base, and one was once observed in the old New York Aquarium traveling 48 inches across the glass front of its tank in eighty-two days.

Sea anemones have few enemies. Some sea stars and sea slugs feed on them, but in general they pursue their quiet lives in peace. Those that live close inshore can survive the falling of the tide by contracting into a tight bunch that opens out with the return of the water. The great majority, however, live below the tidemark.

Stony Corals

The stony corals are the ones whose white skeletons give most of us our idea of what corals are like. It is, in actual fact, a false idea, for *living* corals are not white; their lime skeletons are clothed with flesh of almost every imaginable color and shade.

There are some twenty-five hundred species of coral, mostly in the warm seas of the world, and they form the enormous reefs and atolls of the tropical oceans. One stony coral, the Star Coral, occurs in the latitude of New York and is abundant in Long Island Sound, where it takes the form of little cuplike encrustations on shells and stones.

The Atlantic Red Coral of the Virgin Islands is often exhibited. Its flesh is so brilliantly red that it is outstanding even in reefs that are themselves gaudy.

Skeletons of many corals such as the Atlantic Staghorn Coral, the Elkhorn Coral, or the Pacific Porites Coral are commonly used as tank decorations.

Sea Stars, Brittle Stars, Sea Urchins, Sea Cucumbers

PHYLUM ECHINODERMATA

Five is a magic number among the echinoderms, for basically they are radial animals with five sectors—however disguised. This is quite apparent in the Common Sea Star (or starfish) with its usual five arms.

Echinoderms could also be called "spiny-skinned" animals, for the name comes from the Greek *echinos* for hedgehog and *derma* for skin. Prickliness is most extreme in the long-spined sea urchins and is not apparent at all in the flabby sea cucumbers.

Certain groups such as the sea stars and brittle stars have a skeleton formed of hinged plates and are thus quite flexible. In the sea urchins and sand dollars the plates are not hinged and in effect form a protective shell around the soft parts. The hard plates are scattered throughout the body of the sea cucumbers, and they are consequently flexible and leathery.

Oddly enough the larvae of the echinoderms are bilateral and free-swimming until they change into radial and creeping adults. Sea cucumbers, however, have given up the radial pattern and lie on their sides—just another example of the many peculiarities of the echinoderms.

Echinoderm reproduction can only be called lackadaisical. Most simply shed their eggs and sperm into the sea and let them find each other. But obviously the system works, for there is no scarcity of echinoderms in the seas of the world, from the tropics to polar waters and from the shallows to great oceanic depths.

Crinoids

ECHINODERMATA: CLASS CRINOIDEA

"Sea lilies" and "feather stars" are common names of the crinoids—highly descriptive, too, for the sea lilies spread their flowerlike arms at the end of a stalk sometimes 20 inches long, and the many-branched feather stars may have two hundred arms. Usually they are attached to the bottom at depths of 600 to 15,000 feet, but they may let go and drift upward or inshore. Feather stars are among the most beautiful of marine creatures in any ocean—not only graceful of form but brilliantly colored.

Sea lilies were far more abundant millions of years ago than they are now; some five thousand fossil forms are known, but only eight hundred species of living crinoids. Sea lilies were believed to be extinct until deep-sea dredging expeditions brought them up late in the last century.

Crinoids are often exhibited, but they have a tendency to hide and are seldom seen. Although they are most abundant in the Indo-Pacific region, some live along the North Atlantic in fairly shallow waters; the Common Feather Star ranges from the Arctic to Florida, and the Gray Feather Star from the Arctic to New York.

Sea Stars
ECHINODERMATA: CLASS ASTEROIDEA

Sea stars, or starfish (both names have been used in English for several centuries), are familiar yet ever-fascinating creatures of the world's seashores, particularly in the Northern Hemisphere. They are bottom-dwellers at depths of a few feet to nearly 20,000 feet, there are nearly 2,000 species, and they have great variety of form, size, and color.

The basic form is a central body disk with five more or less symmetrical arms radiating from it, but some have many more arms, and others are almost perfect pentagons. As for size, there

Edged sea stars of the Indo-Pacific. RENÉ L. A. CATALA PHOTO.

217

are miniature stars scarcely half an inch across and 3-foot giants. Red, yellow, orange, and pink are the common colors, but there are also gray, green, blue, and purple stars.

The mouth and stomach are in the central disk—the mouth on the lower side—and on top is a porous plate through which water enters and circulates. The underside of the arms bears hundreds of small "tube feet," constantly in motion, and by means of them the star can creep slowly in any direction and over any surface, even up the glass wall of an aquarium tank.

Sea stars are expert at feeding on shellfish and do enormous damage to oyster beds. Anyone who has tried to open an oyster or a clam, even with a special knife, may be surprised that a sea star does it with ease. It simply folds its arms over the shellfish, hundreds of tube feet attach their terminal suction disks to each half of the shell, and a strong muscular pull begins. A large sea star can exert a pull of 7 to 10 pounds, and as soon as a slight aperture appears between the halves, the star pushes its stomach through the opening and begins to feed. The process is about the same if the victim is a marine worm or a small fish; the tube feet hold it, and the stomach enfolds its prey.

When a sea star is turned on its back, it has several ways of righting itself. It may bend its arms backward to raise the central disk until it becomes top-heavy and topples over, or it may bend all its arms in one direction and finally roll over, or it may bend some arms under the body until the tube feet take hold—it then literally crawls under itself until the unattached side flips over.

Edged Sea Stars

The edged sea stars are mostly deep-sea animals and are distinguished by having a sharp boundary between their upper and lower surfaces. The Vermilion Sea Star of Pacific shores from Alaska to California is conspicuous in any surroundings, for its color is intense. It is 3 to 7 inches in diameter. One of the more spectacular Atlantic stars is the Giant Sea Star of Florida and the West Indies, with a disk 5 inches thick and arms that give it a breadth of 18 to 20 inches. It is commonly yellow, but it may be orange or green, maroon or purple, and speckled with yellow spots where the plates of the skeleton join each other.

Spiny Sea Stars

Almost all spiny sea stars have more than five arms, usually seven to seventeen, and are more or less covered above and below with conspicuous but short spines. Some are called sun stars and actually do look like stylized representations of the sun, with a broad central disk and seven to thirteen broad-based, tapering arms and a mingling of brilliant colors on the upper surface. The

Common Sun Star of northern waters around the world is often scarlet in the center of the disk with a surrounding band of crimson to the bases of the arms, which are banded in pink and white and tipped with crimson. The Pacific Sun Star of Alaska to California is much less colorful, mostly a dull blue-gray, and its eight to thirteen arms are quite slender.

See page 220

The New York Aquarium usually exhibits the red, yellow, or purplish Broad-disk Sea Star, or Sea Bat, of the Northwest Pacific coast. Its arms are rather short, but no less efficient for all that; it has been recorded as eating seaweed, sponges, sea urchins, and even minute diatoms. A 10-inch specimen is a large one.

Thanks to speedy air travel, the interesting Crown of Thorns Sea Star of the Hawaii-Indo-Pacific region is now often exhibited. It may be 14 inches in diameter, with as many as sixteen arms covered with venomous spines. Brown or yellow, it is not particularly spectacular, but it is important in its native waters because it feeds on coral animals and in some places is actually destroying reefs. There is a marine conservation lesson to be

See page 220

Broad-disc Sea Stars, or Sea Bats

Rose Sea Star; a spiny sea star

Crown of Thorns Sea Star

Pacific Sun Star

Blood Sea Star; a spiny sea star

Mottled Sea Star; a forceps-carrying sea star

Common Sea Star, or Starfish

learned here. The natural enemy of the Crown of Thorns Sea Star is the Triton, or Trumpet Shell, a huge marine snail. But Triton Shells are relentlessly collected for sale as souvenirs, the sea stars thrive under reduced predation—and the coral reefs are slowly being nibbled away.

Forceps-carrying Sea Stars

These sea stars (which include many common ones along the North Atlantic coast) have small pincerlike spines on the upper surface of the body; sea urchins are the only other animals that have them. As a rule the North Atlantic members of the group have five arms, but some in the Pacific have as many as twenty-four.

The Common Sea Star of Maine to the Gulf of Mexico is hated by proprietors of oyster beds and harvesters of clams. Baby sea stars settle on seaweed and eelgrass and feed on the baby shellfish that live in the same habitat; one little star was observed eating fifty young clams in six days. Feeding so heavily, they develop rapidly, and at the end of their first year may have arms 2½ inches long and be ready to spawn. Adults are 6 to 11 inches in diameter.

Colors are variable in the Common Sea Star and range through brown, purple, bronze, green, and orange.

Like other sea stars, the Common Sea Star can regenerate an arm that is accidentally broken off—or even all its arms.

Brittle Stars and Basket Stars
ECHINODERMATA: CLASS OPHIUROIDEA

Brittle Stars

Brittle stars are so called because their long, slender, highly flexible arms break off so readily when they are grasped. They are also called serpent stars from the snakelike wriggling motion of their arms.

All are small, with a body disk only about 1 inch in diameter, but the arms may be 6 to 15 inches long. Writhing and wriggling, curling an arm around rocks or coral or seaweed and pulling themselves along, brittle stars roam over every type of bottom in all seas, from the shallows to great depths. There are some sixteen hundred species, and many are brightly colored.

Many species of brittle star are found along the North Atlantic coast, and one often exhibited is the grayish-bluish-white Long-armed Brittle Star, a fragile little creature whose body disk *See page 222* is only about one-fifth of an inch in diameter and whose arms are only 1½ inches long. Like some other brittle stars, it is hermaphroditic: both sexes are found in the same animal. It ranges from the Arctic to Long Island.

*Long-armed
Brittle Star*

The Daisy Brittle Star of the same range is nearly three times as large, and while its color is variable, it is often reddish on the disk with the arms banded in red and white.

Brittle stars are wary creatures, and although they are not known to have eyes, they sense an intruder and scuttle into a crevice for safety.

Basket Stars

If any sea creature can be thought of as a plant, it is the Basket Star. It is *not* a plant, of course, but when it unfurls its multibranched arms, first like the "fiddle heads" of ferns and then full out like a filmy miniature tree, its resemblance to a graceful plant is so striking that visitors to the Aquarium often ask what kind of plant it is. It even "wilts" like a plant, when the arms contract into a tangled mass around the five-sided body disk.

Basket Stars live along the shores of the North Atlantic and in the Bahamas from just below the low-water mark to depths of half a mile. By day they are curled up and difficult to find, but they are easily seen at night when they "walk" on the tips of their arms. They feed on minute plankton and in the Aquarium readily eat brine shrimp; when a brine shrimp blunders against one of the filmy tips, the tip curls around it, the arm "wilts," and the prey is carried to the mouth.

When the Basket Star was described by Governor John Winthrop of Connecticut in 1670, he counted the branching of the arms and found there were 81,920 terminal branches.

OPPOSITE: *Basket Star*

Sea Urchins and Sand Dollars
ECHINODERMATA: CLASS ECHINOIDEA

Sea Urchins

"Urchin" is a very old English name for the hedgehog, and its application to the prickliest of all echinoderms is certainly apt. Some sea urchins have spines a foot long.

Sea urchins are most abundant in Arctic waters, literally carpeting the bottom in some places, but there are more species in the world's tropics and subtropics. The body is contained in a skeleton shaped much like a doorknob studded with movable spines; the mouth with its five teeth is in the center of the lower surface. Some species travel on their rows of tube feet, others "walk" on the tips of their spines at the surprising speed of about 1 inch a second.

The well-named Hatpin Sea Urchin of the tropical Atlantic and the Mediterranean has venomous spines about a foot long. Body muscles keep them in constant motion, describing little circles, and when a shadow falls across the black body, a cluster of spines points toward it. The barbed tips penetrate the skin at the slightest touch and then break off. The severe stinging sensation they produce is not fatal, but it is extremely painful, and the soft lime of the tip usually crumbles when an attempt is made to remove it with tweezers.

One of the commonest sea urchins along the Atlantic coast is the Purple Sea Urchin of Cape Cod to Mexico, about 1¾ inches in diameter with ¾-inch spines. It is a valuable experimental animal for biological research, and great numbers are used in the Osborn Laboratories of Marine Sciences for testing toxic substances from the sea. Much that is known about the fertilization and development of an egg of any kind comes from the studies of the Purple Sea Urchin.

Sand Dollars

Beachcombers know the Sand Dollar well, for its bleached skeleton is commonly found along the shores of the North Atlantic from New Jersey to the Arctic Ocean and in the Pacific from Vancouver Island to Japan. The skeleton is a circular, thin, limy wafer, the upper surface marked with a slightly raised five-rayed star. In life, the Sand Dollar is covered with dense, short spines that feel velvety to the touch. Tiny tube feet on the undersurface enable it to move slowly and burrow into the sand, where it feeds on algae, diatoms, and other minute life.

The Common Sand Dollar of the New York area is about 3 inches in diameter and is extremely abundant on sandy bottoms in some areas; thousands may be cast up on the beach after a storm.

Sand Dollar

Indelible ink was once made from Sand Dollars by extracting the purple-brown pigment that colors the living animal.

The Sand Dollar is seldom exhibited because it tends to bury itself in the sandy bottom of its tank.

Sea Cucumbers
ECHINODERMATA: CLASS HOLOTHUROIDEA

Sea cucumbers have three special claims to fame. Many kinds voluntarily cast out most of their internal organs when they are provoked, some give shelter inside their body to small Pearlfish, and some secrete a virulent poison that will quickly kill other fish—but not the Pearlfish in normal circumstances. The poison, called Holothurin, is under intensive study as a potentially valuable "drug from the sea."

Pliny the Elder named them "sea cucumbers" nearly nineteen hundred years ago, and the name has stuck because it is so descriptive. (In more modern times one of the smaller sea cucumbers has been given the common name of "sea gherkin.") They are plump, flabby, not very attractively colored creatures that lie on muddy bottoms of the world's cold and temperate as well as tropical seas, gently waving plumy tentacles at the feeding end to draw mud into the mouth and expelling the debris through the cloaca at the other end.

Sea Cucumber

Evisceration, or expelling of the internal organs, is believed to be a defensive mechanism, for some organs come out of the cloaca in the form of sticky threads that quickly envelop an attacking fish. Evisceration can be induced by keeping a sea cucumber in water warmer than it normally prefers, as well as by rough handling. The cast-off organs grow again in four to six weeks.

How the Pearlfish gains and keeps its immunity to the sea cucumber's poison, and why it does not trigger evisceration when it slips into the sheltering body cavity through the cloaca, are not understood. Under artificial circumstances, as when a Pearlfish is put into a tank cloudy with a mucous secretion from a sea cucumber, it will die, although not nearly as rapidly as other fish.

A Sea Cucumber of Florida and the Bahamas occasionally reaches a length of 40 inches and a diameter of 8 inches. Much longer and more slender is the Snake-like Sea Cucumber of Hawaii, which is often exhibited.

Boiled, dried, or smoked sea cucumbers are standard items of food in the Orient and South Pacific under the names of "trepang" or "bêche-de-mer."

Segmented Sea Worms
PHYLUM ANNELIDA: CLASS POLYCHAETA

The annelids are the segmented sea worms. Those known as Clam Worms are prized by coastal fishermen as excellent bait —and experienced fishermen know how to pick them up without being nipped by the strong pincerlike jaws. The Clam Worm of both sides of the North Atlantic is found also along the Pacific coast. It is common in muddy beaches, living in mucous-lined burrows, and attains a length of 18 inches. A relative on the Pacific coast reaches 3 feet in length and is as thick—and active— as a garter snake as it propels itself through the water by means of the paddlelike extensions from each of its many segments.

The Atlantic Clam Worm is olive brown or olive blue and has a pearly, iridescent quality. It feeds on the bottom at night, scavenging on dead clams and the like, and burrows in the mud by day. It is often exhibited, but its burrowing habit makes it hard to see.

Perhaps the most famous of the sea worms is the Palolo of Samoa and a few other localities in the South Pacific that swarms to the surface in enormous numbers twice a year, in October and November, on the sixth to the eighth day after the full moon. The whole worm is about 16 inches long, but at swarming time the posterior three-fourths breaks off and rises to the surface from coral reefs under the water. Here the reproductive bodies wriggle about for an hour or two until the saclike bodies burst, and sperm and eggs are released. Within three days the newly formed creatures sink down to the reef, to repeat the process the following year. The swarming is eagerly anticipated by the natives of Samoa, who wait on the shore to harvest the fragile bodies in every kind of container—and even to gulp them down raw.

Anyone who sees a furry little mouse moving about on the floor of an Aquarium tank can be sure he is looking at a Sea Mouse, one of the annelids that has assumed an oval shape, is covered with hairlike bristles with a shimmering iridescence, and scurries about in the mud by means of about forty pairs of legs. It is found from Long Island northward.

"Feather-duster worm" is the general common name for a large number of marine worms—a name bestowed because they

Feather-duster Worm of the Indo-Pacific. RENÉ L. A. CATALA PHOTO.

227

so obviously resemble feather dusters. A parchmentlike stalk, often several inches long, protrudes from the sand and is crowned, when the animal is feeding, with feathery plumes that trap minute organisms in the water. Usually they are extremely sensitive to disturbances — even a shadow passing over them — and quickly draw the gill plumes into the tube, but "blossom" and resume feeding in a few minutes. Feather-duster worms are found in most seas and are often brightly colored.

Joint-legged Animals
PHYLUM ARTHROPODA

No matter what other animals we know, we *all* know arthropods, the joint-legged animals. Even if we don't know those that live in water (some thirty-five thousand species), we can't escape knowing some of the 880,000 species that live on land. Most of those are the insects.

Only some of the best-known sea-dwelling arthropods will be discussed here. In general it can be said of all arthropods that they have an outer shell (such as that of a lobster) that is shed periodically as they grow and that they have jointed legs.

Horseshoe Crabs
ARTHROPODA: CLASS XIPHOSURIDA

It is always nice to have an abundance of something your friends want and to be able to give it away freely. Aquariums and marine stations from Maine to Yucatan are in that happy position in regard to Horseshoe Crabs. There is only a single species along this entire coastline, plus a few relatives on the shores of southeastern Asia, and since they are strange-looking animals very like their fossil relatives of 175 million years ago, European aquariums are always glad to have a few as gifts or exchanges. Collecting them is just a matter of wading along the beach and picking them up.

Despite their name, they are not crabs, but are perhaps descendants of the trilobites that flourished in the age when coal was being formed. They are actually more closely related to land-dwelling spiders and scorpions. Sometimes called King Crabs, they are not to be confused with the commercial King Crab of the North Pacific.

They are bottom-dwellers, moving on five pairs of jointed legs or swimming with flapping motions of the plates that cover the gills underneath and at the rear of the leathery shell, and at the same time jerking the legs. The mouth is on the underside of the almost circular shell, and close to it are spines on the walking legs and other appendages that help break up food and shove it into the mouth. Horseshoe Crabs eat dead fish, marine worms,

bivalves, seaweed, and other such organic material that they find _Horseshoe Crabs_
on the bottom, and are valuable scavengers.

They have four eyes, two of them compound and widely separated on the upper shell and two close together and well forward. The tail spine is long and hard and can be moved sideways and up and down; when a Horseshoe Crab is on its back, a prying motion of the tail spine enables it to turn over easily. The sharp-pointed tail is not venomous.

A Horseshoe Crab molts its old shell as it grows, literally walking out of it when it splits along the forward edge. Discarded shells are found, sometimes by the thousands, along the beaches.

The living animals are trapped in some areas and used as food for hogs and chickens or as fertilizer.

Crustaceans

ARTHROPODA: CLASS CRUSTACEA

"Crustacean" is a catchall name for twenty-five thousand joint-legged animals, most of which live in salt or fresh water; a few dwell on land. Crustaceans include lobsters and crabs and shrimps and crayfish that are familiar to almost everyone, the barnacles that foul the bottoms of ships and encrust rocks and pilings in the sea, and a vast variety of other creatures better known to specialists than to anyone else.

Barnacles

Barnacles start life as free-swimming little larvae, and after seven molts they acquire a pair of stalked eyes and a pair of hinged shells. By then they are ready to settle down for life on a rock or any convenient anchorage. A barnacle, as one zoologist wrote, is "a crustacean which is fastened by its head, lies on its back, and kicks food into its mouth."

Goose Barnacles

The kicking is done by means of feathery and jointed legs that are thrust out of the shell and sweep minute organisms into the mouth. The Common Atlantic, or Acorn, Barnacles of the region between high and low tides on both sides of the North Atlantic encrust the rocks with millions of individuals and close their shells tightly when the tide is out, but open and resume feeding as soon as they are again covered with water. Less than half an inch in diameter, their feeding feet are not easily observed, but their behavior is quite apparent in the Giant Barnacle of the eastern Pacific, whose shell may be 3 inches high and 5 or 6 inches in diameter. Its feet sweep in 2-inch swaths.

Some barnacles are attached by means of a tough, fleshy stalk, usually to a floating object, and are called Goose Barnacles because in medieval times geese were believed to hatch from them. Goose Barnacles may be 2 inches long and are a severe drag on ships in the tropical oceans.

A special laboratory connected with the New York Aquarium is studying the life history of barnacles with the hope of reducing the marine fouling problem, and also to determine the nature of the barnacle's attachment cement.

Shrimps, Lobsters, and Crabs

Hundreds of thousands of tons of shrimps, lobsters, and crabs are harvested from the sea every year to supply the market for seafood at least 100,000 tons of the American Shrimp alone are taken each year in Florida and the Gulf of Mexico by netting, and lobster and crab traps make a living for thousands in more northern waters.

Like other crustaceans, shrimps and lobsters and crabs shed their shells as they grow and for a time are soft-bodied and helpless. These are the soft-shelled crabs of seafood markets.

Large American Shrimps are often called prawns, but there is a true Prawn, much used for food, that is taken in eelgrass and salt marches along the Atlantic coast. The small but interesting Snapping Shrimps, about 1¾ inches long, range from Virginia to Brazil. One claw is enormously enlarged, and when the two blades are snapped shut, the sound is as loud as the explosion of a small firecracker. Some tropical shrimps (which may be quite prettily colored, even candy-striped in red) are known as "cleaning shrimps" from their habit of grooming fishes to remove parasites. One often exhibited is the Red-backed Cleaning Shrimp. *See page 232*

The American Lobster is such a valuable food resource that it has been extensively studied in an effort to increase its numbers by artificial rearing. The usual market size is 1½ to 2 pounds, but a 34-pound giant is on record. The most usual color of the upper part of the shell is dull green, with yellow to orange

Red-backed Cleaning Shrimp

below, but occasionally a lobster is caught that is bright blue or red (as the shell becomes when a lobster is boiled) or even mottled red and black. Millions of lobsters are taken every year off New England and Canada.

The American Lobster often burrows to await its prey of living small fishes—although like other lobsters, it is a great scavenger on dead material. It digs holes about 2 feet deep, enters tailfirst, and lies in wait with its great pincers extended.

Lobster eggs are laid in midsummer and are carried by the female, adhering to the underside of the tail, until the following summer. A 17-inch female was found to have sixty-three thousand eggs. There is enormous mortality after the transparent,

OPPOSITE: *Spiny Lobsters*

Blue color phase of the North American Lobster
Fiddler Crabs

shrimplike little lobsters hatch and swim at the surface. After three molts they assume adult form and sink to the bottom.

In the southern Atlantic and the West Indies the com- *See page 233* mon lobster is the Spiny Lobster, which lacks the heavy pincers that help make the American Lobster such good eating. Its long legs and very long, whiplike antennae make it a spectacular exhibit. The edible flesh is concentrated in the tail muscles, and only this part is sold commercially.

Around Florida and the West Indies (occasionally to the New York area) is the peculiar Locust Lobster or Sea Roach, whose female is much larger than the male and is sometimes 3 feet long. It moves slowly over the bottom and is most active at night. It is considered good food in the West Indies.

The crab usually sold in food markets is the Blue Crab of the coast from Cape Cod to Florida and around the edge of the Gulf to Mississippi—second only to the lobster in economic importance. Many crabs are rather prettily colored; this one is in general dark green, with bright blue on the legs, and is sometimes streaked with scarlet.

A striking crab usually exhibited at the Aquarium is the Long-eyed Swimming Crab of Hawaii, some 5 inches broad, with eyes at the end of long stalks protected by a groove at the front of the shell. It is one of the largest swimming crabs in Hawaii and is excellent eating.

Anyone who has spent time along the New England shores and salt marshes knows one or more species of Fiddler Crab, for fiddlers abound in sandy or muddy places and are easily recognized by the very large claw of the male, held horizontally across the front of the body and usually moving with short, jerky motions; the other claw, the "fiddler's bow," is much more slender.

Fiddler Crabs are found in similar mud or sand habitats all over the world. They live in burrows that they dig themselves, sometimes to a depth of 3 feet. New England fiddlers are 1 to 1½ inches across; some tropical species are twice that size.

Male fiddlers use the large claw in defense and in courtship gestures. If the large claw is torn off—as it may be when it clamps onto an attacker—a "bow" claw develops on that side at the next molt, and the former bow becomes a large claw, so that fiddlers may be either right-handed or left-handed.

The small Hermit Crabs of our coast are noted for their *See page 237* fickleness in house-hunting. The soft and unprotected abdomen is inserted in an empty shell, often that of a periwinkle or a mud snail, and the shell goes bumping along behind whenever the crab travels. It must, of course, find a larger home as it grows, and it investigates pretty nearly any shell it finds—usually to discover that it already has a tenant.

The well-named Box Crab of the Atlantic tropics (occasionally ranging to Massachusetts) is so well protected when its legs are pulled in and its broad claws are held close that it really is boxlike. It may be about 4 inches across and is buff or purplish with a network of purplish streaks.

The very long-legged Spider Crabs move about in the water with spiderlike deliberation. If they *were* spiders, with a spider's venom, some of them would be truly frightening; the Japanese Spider Crab, for example, has a leg-spread of 12 feet. Some of those along the Atlantic shore can span 18 inches. A common habit is that of placing bits of seaweed on the back, so that the crab is well concealed when it is among sea vegetation.

The King Crab of the North Pacific, from Washington to Alaska, cannot compete with the Japanese Spider Crab in leg-span, but it is a monster nevertheless, with a body that may be the size of a dinner plate and powerful legs as thick as a man's wrist. King Crab meat is an expensive delicacy in seafood restaurants, and only the flesh extracted from the legs is eaten.

Mantis Shrimps

A Mantis Shrimp does not stand reared on its legs, spiny claws at the ready, like the Praying Mantis for which it is named, but it does hold its claws, which in general resemble those of the mantis, in the same way. Creeping about on the bottom or lying in a burrow, the Mantis Shrimp waits for a fish to swim within reach — and then with a lightning-quick flick of the blades the prey is seized and may even be cut in two.

Mantis Shrimps are common from Cape Cod to Florida, below the low-water mark, and there are usually several openings to their burrows. They are pale-colored, often tinted with rose or green. There are some two hundred species over the world, ranging from 2 inches to 12 inches in length.

Mantis Shrimp of the Indo-Pacific. RENÉ L. A. CATALA PHOTO.

Hermit Crab
Spider Crab

Mollusks
PHYLUM MOLLUSCA

"Mollusk" means "shellfish" to most of us, and the term is obviously appropriate when we think of oysters, clams, scallops, mussels, and abalones; it may seem less so when we consider that squids and octopuses are also mollusks. Some mollusks spend their lives in a protective shell, and others have a shell only at the earliest larval stage or have the merest rudiment of an internal shell as adults. The word "mollusk" really means soft-bodied, from the Latin *mollis*, meaning soft.

Mollusks are an enormous group of animals, some forty thousand species, of extremely ancient origin — in fact, as many fossil kinds are known as living species. They live in water and on land all over the world. Spiral-shelled snails and slimy slugs are mollusks — although in the latter the shell is reduced to a token plate.

Snails
MOLLUSCA: CLASS GASTROPODA

See page 240

Moon Snails take their common name from the crescent-moon shape of their egg masses; Sand-collar Snail is another name, for when the eggs are extruded and passed over the rear of the body whorl onto the sand, sand grains stick to them, and the whole mass becomes a sandy, capelike collar studded with transparent dots that are the eggs. Sand collars — the egg masses — are often found on the shore, but they crumble easily.

The most remarkable thing about the Moon Snail is the size of its foot, with which it creeps over the sand or ploughs its way through the soft bottom. Even though the Moon Snail's shell may be 3 or 4 inches high, it seems impossible that such a huge foot could be drawn into it. Nevertheless, it can withdraw the foot very quickly when disturbed.

Moon Snails are abundant along the coast from the Gulf of St. Lawrence to North Carolina in shallow water and between tides. They can be destructive to clams, clinging to them with their foot and boring into the shell with their rasping tongue. Several species are common in warm waters, as around the Florida Keys.

Scallops and Clams
MOLLUSCA: CLASS BIVALVIA

Scallops

Scallops are clams that swim by jet propulsion. Nothing would seem more inert than a scallop lying on the bottom — but let a sea star come creeping along on its tube feet, and the scallop takes off with a soaring burst of speed, hinged side forward, by clapping the halves of its shell.

In medieval times scallop shells were the symbol of pilgrims, who picked them up on the shores of Galicia and used them as spoons or cups; today they are better known all over the world as the symbol of a large oil company. Gourmets, of course, know the thick, sweet, tasty muscle that is the edible part of the Common Scallop.

Tons of Common Scallops are harvested every year from Cape Hatteras to Cape Cod. They are most abundant in the northern part of their range. Most are 2 to 3 inches in diameter, gray or white, yellowish brown or reddish.

The Rough Lima of the tropical Atlantic has overlapping *See page 240* scales on its shell so that it is sometimes called the File-shell Scallop. The soft parts and the ring of tentacles around the edges of the open shell are brilliant scarlet—hence an alternative name, Flame Scallop. The usual size is 2 to 5 inches, and Rough Limas are found from North Carolina to the West Indies.

The largest scallop of the Atlantic coast is the Deep Sea Scallop, which is 5 to 6 inches across the shell. It is found from New Jersey to Labrador and is most abundant off the coast of Maine at depths of 60 to 600 feet. The large shells are often used as baking plates for seafood.

Deep Sea Scallop

Florida Moon Snail. The living snail has been arbitrarily placed inside the egg mass for comparison of size. ALICE S. KESLER PHOTO.

Rough Lima, or Flame Scallop

Clams

Even the burrowing clams — the Soft-shell and the Quahog, or Little-neck — are swimmers at one stage of their lives. As larvae they swim freely, but soon settle down on seaweed, rocks, or shells, and then drop to the bottom and bury themselves when they are about a quarter of an inch long.

The Soft-shell Clam lives in the muddy or sandy bottom of sheltered bays or estuaries between high and low tide from the Carolinas to the Arctic and also along the shores of northern Europe. Its muscular foot enables it to burrow to a shallow depth, and it lies buried with the "neck," or siphon, pointed upward. The neck may be a foot long and has two openings, one to carry diatom-laden water into the gill chamber and the other to expel digested food.

The Quahog has a much harder shell and a very short "neck." It is much used for making clam chowder; quite small Quahogs are served in restaurants as Little-necks or Cherrystones. The Quahog has about the same range as the Soft-shell, but is not found so far north.

In both the siphon can be drawn into the shell, which closes tightly at low tide.

Octopuses and Relatives
MOLLUSCA: CLASS CEPHALOPODA

In the early years of this century the respected director of a marine biological laboratory allowed his emotions to run away with him when he discussed the octopuses.

"Nothing in nature," he wrote, "is more gruesome and hideous than the sinuous writhing of these creatures, or more strangely fascinating than the wonderful play of varied colors over their soft, pulsating bodies, this movement contrasted all the time with the cruel, stony stare of their expressionless eyes."

Well, maybe. Certainly he had precedents for the loathing he so obviously felt; Victor Hugo called the octopus "a disease embodied in monstrosity," and even today it is often referred to as the Devilfish.

Actually, octopuses are shy, timid, and retiring and not at all fond of wrapping their eight arms around a skin diver and strangling him—although skin divers who have captured octopuses do say it is a little difficult to get free of the arms with their double row of sucker disks. It is usually impossible to make an octopus bite, but there are two Australian species whose venomous bites have paralyzing effects that have killed two or three people.

The body of an octopus is the flabby, baglike structure from which the arms radiate, and the only hard parts are the sharp teeth, rather like a parrot's beak. The octopus uses these to crush the fishes, crustaceans, and other mollusks that it seizes with its sucker-bearing arms. Normally they hide in rocky crevices with the arms ready to snake out and make a capture, or they may give chase by a jet-propelled dart backward.

Looked at just as an interesting creature of the sea and not as "a disease embodied in monstrosity," an octopus can actually be rather attractive. Certainly it is sinuously graceful in its movements, and the flickering changes of color when it is excited may be compared—not exactly to the play of Northern Lights!—but to a living kaleidoscope. Tiny sacs of pigment lie in the thin skin, and special muscles pull the sacs flat; thus, they appear as red, yellow, blue, green, and brown spots about one-sixteenth of an inch in diameter. These come and go over the body in waves, so that the octopus seems to shiver in technicolor.

Octopuses are good mothers. Their eggs are attached to underwater objects and guarded by the female for as long as three months, during which she tends them assiduously, not even taking time out to eat.

Four species of octopus are found along the Atlantic coast as far north as Cape Cod, but even those of Florida waters are small, measured in inches rather than feet.

OPPOSITE: *Giant Pacific Octopus*

Giant Pacific Octopus guarding its eggs. U. ERICH FRIESE PHOTO.

Much larger is the Giant Pacific Octopus quite common in Puget Sound. It lives in crevices among rocks in shallow water, and its usual method of registering protest at intrusion is to eject a stream of black "ink." All octopuses and squids can do that, incidentally.

A 40-pound Pacific Octopus with an arm-spread of 10 feet has been exhibited at the New York Aquarium. In preparation for shipping by air, it was gradually cooled in water almost at the freezing point, put in a plastic bag of 10 gallons of cold water and an atmosphere of pure oxygen, and packed in ice. Pacific Octopuses are exhibited at the Aquarium in sea water kept under 50° F at all times.

In the economy of the sea the backward-darting, cigar-shaped squids are perhaps most valuable as food for fishes, sperm whales, and seals. In man's economy they make wonderful fish bait, especially for the cod fishing industry.

Squids are capable of extremely fast backward-darting by means of water expelled from the mantle cavity under the head. Thus they pursue their prey, seize it with their sucker-bearing arms, and bite it to death. They are not averse to biting a fisherman's hand.

The largest living invertebrate is the Giant Squid of the cold northern oceans, occasionally 50 feet long.

In the same group as the octopus and squid is the Common Cuttlefish of the Mediterranean and eastern Atlantic whose limy internal shell is the "cuttlefish bone" given to pet cagebirds.

One of the few cephalopods celebrated in poetry is the "Chambered Nautilus" of Oliver Wendell Holmes's poem:

> ". . . the ship of pearl, which, poets feign,
> Sails the unshadowed main, – "

Holmes was naturalist enough to know that poets "feigned" the Chambered Nautilus as sailing; actually it does not float on the surface, but swims or crawls over the bottom in the tropical Pacific and Indian Oceans.

The Chordates
PHYLUM CHORDATA: CLASS ASCIDIACEA

Sea Squirts, or Tunicates

The chordates are the point at which the invertebrates almost merge with the vertebrates, or backboned animals. In fact, except for the sea squirts and two other groups called salps and lancets all chordates are backboned.

When they are in their larval stage and look somewhat like tadpoles, sea squirts and their close relatives have a firm but flexible structure called a notochord running through the body rather like a backbone, although it is merely tough and gelatinous, not bony.

The squat, rounded body of the adult sea squirt, about an inch in diameter, with two rather short projecting siphons, gives it one of its common names, Sea Grape. It is more appropriately called Sea Squirt because of the two jets of water it forcibly ejects from the siphons when it is disturbed.

At least one species of sea squirt grows naturally in the New York Aquarium's filter beds and tanks, probably having been introduced in sea water or objects brought in from the sea. There they no doubt provide some filtration for the circulating water by removing the minute organisms on which they feed.

A very large number of reptiles are more or less aquatic, but only a few are customarily exhibited in aquariums; many more are likely to be found in zoological parks. Here only the sea turtles and the sea snakes will be discussed.

Sea Turtles
ORDER CHELONIA: DERMOCHELIDAE

The largest sea turtle is the huge Leatherback of all seas, sometimes 8 feet long and 1,500 pounds in weight. Its name comes from its smooth, leathery skin in which bony platelets are embedded. Like other sea turtles, it spends its whole life in the water except when the female comes ashore to deposit her eggs in a hole dug with the flippers above the high-tide line on a sandy beach. The eggs are then covered with sand, and after hatching, the little turtles race for the water.

Leatherbacks are rarely exhibited; denizens of the deep sea, their freedom limited only by continents and islands, they cannot adjust to the confines of even the largest restraining tank.

True Sea Turtles
CHELONIA: CHELONIIDAE

The so-called True Sea Turtles are those possessing a hard shell. They include the Green, Loggerhead, Ridley, and Hawksbill Turtles. They live in most tropical and subtropical seas. Some are largely vegetarian, others are mainly carnivorous and eat crabs, conchs, clams, oysters, jellyfish, sponges, and fish.

Green Turtles, which have both Atlantic and Pacific races, have long been hunted for their meat, which is used in making turtle soup; this turtle has, indeed, been called "the most valuable reptile in the world." Key West, Florida, is the center of the Green Turtle "industry" in the United States. Most turtles nowadays weigh 75 to 150 pounds, but an 850-pound specimen was once caught in the West Indies.

See page 248

The Atlantic and Pacific races of the Loggerhead wander considerably along the coasts, preferring shallow bays. This is perhaps the most omnivorous of all the sea turtles.

The Atlantic Ridley, ranging from the Gulf of Mexico to *See page 248* Massachusetts, is the smallest of the sea turtles, about 28 inches maximum. Its Pacific race, in the warmer parts of the Indian and Pacific Oceans, is slightly larger.

Commercial tortoiseshell comes from the Hawksbill Turtle of the world's warm seas. It is not large. The length is about 3 feet, and the weight some 160 pounds. Removal of the tortoise-shell plates generally results in the death of the turtle.

The eggs of all sea turtles are highly prized for food, and the flesh of most is quite palatable.

Hawksbill

Green Turtle

Atlantic Ridley

Young Atlantic
Loggerhead

Sea Snakes
ORDER SQUAMATA: SUBORDER SERPENTES: HYDROPHIIDAE

All sea snakes are highly venomous, but they use their venom to kill fishes and small eels and are seldom a danger to man except in unusual circumstances. There are fifty species in the tropical Indian and Pacific Oceans, and they are not found in the Atlantic.

Most sea snakes spend their entire lives in the water and are beautifully adapted for that life; the tail is flattened from side to side almost like an oar, and the snakes are extremely agile swimmers. Great numbers are sometimes seen basking at the surface in the Pacific Ocean. The young are born alive in the water, except in a few species that deposit eggs in sea caves.

The American herpetologist Clifford H. Pope wrote of the sea snakes that "they are at once the most venomous and the most harmless of poisonous snakes." Their venom is chiefly neurotoxic—that is, it acts on the nervous system and may stop heart or lung action—and that of at least one species is more potent than the venom of an Indian Cobra. Yet most sea snakes are not aggressive and seldom attack bathers; fishermen are said to pick them out of their nets with bare hands.

The only species that reaches the western shores of the Americas is the Yellow-bellied Sea Snake, about 3 feet long. Like other sea snakes, it is difficult to keep in captivity.

Yellow-bellied Sea Snakes. SAN DIEGO ZOO PHOTO.

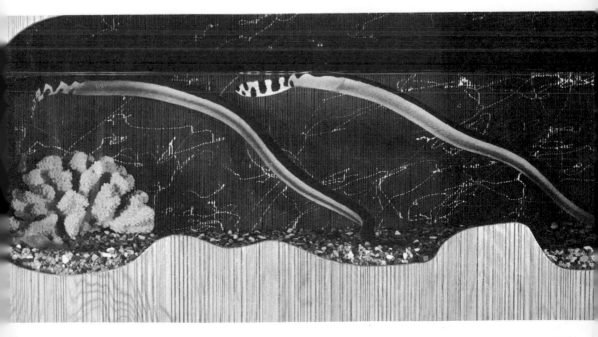

BIRDS

So many birds are bound to the water in one way or another, especially in their search for food, that it is hard to draw a line for discussion in a book such as this. However, penguins and pelicans, gannets, cormorants, and puffins are fairly representative of a way of life that depends upon the seas, and they also adapt readily to exhibition in aquariums, so the line will arbitrarily be drawn there.

Penguins
ORDER SPHENISCIFORMES: SPHENISCIDAE

Penguins cannot fly, but this is no handicap to the seventeen species. Propelled by wings that have become flippers, they streak through the water at speeds of up to an estimated 30 miles an hour—more than enough to catch fish, squids, shrimps, and cuttlefish.

Except for the Galápagos Penguin precariously existing on two or three small islands at the Equator, penguins are confined to the Antarctic ice shelf and its adjacent cold seas and frozen islands or follow chill oceanic currents along the shores of southern Africa, South America, Australia, and New Zealand.

Very few birds are likened to people in any way—except penguins. "A little man in a full dress suit" comes inevitably to mind as we watch a sleekly groomed, gravely sedate, black and white penguin, and the few that have a suffusion of orange-red around the head and upper breast and bill, or a head tuft of feathers, only strengthen the illusion. Penguins are not, of course, quite as sedate as they seem to be when simply standing around waiting for something to happen; they can bite viciously and pummel an intruder with their wings or tear the air with braying calls. Indeed, the Black-footed Penguin is often called the Jackass Penguin because of its unlovely braying voice.

Penguins are superbly at home in the water, but they must come ashore to build their crude nests of stones or sticks or to deposit their eggs in burrows. There are one or two eggs, depending on the species, and the downy chicks are fed by the parents on regurgitated food brought from the sea.

OPPOSITE: *Emperor Penguins at Cape Crozier, Antarctica.* CARLETON RAY PHOTO.

Magellan Penguin in nest burrow. WILLIAM G. CONWAY PHOTO.

Humboldt Penguins

OPPOSITE: *Emperor Penguins "tobogganing."* W. R. CURTSINGER PHOTO.

On land, snow, or ice penguins are seemingly awkward as they waddle, hop, or make bellybuster slides propelled by feet and flippers, and yet an Adelie Penguin can walk at a rate of three miles an hour, waddle-run at twice that speed, and outdistance a running man when it "toboggans."

Enemies are comparatively few. Leopard Seals and Killer Whales may attack penguins in the water, and Skuas, Sheath-bills, and Giant Petrels make tireless raids on eggs and chicks in the rookeries, but so vast are their numbers that predation is inconsequential.

See pages 251, 252
The largest species is the Emperor Penguin, nearly 4 feet tall and weighing as much as 90 pounds, strikingly beautiful with delicate golden tints around its head. It breeds on the shores of Antarctica, and during the winter, when the temperature may drop to −40° F, the male cradles the single egg on his feet for sixty-two to sixty-four days, fasting all the while. The somewhat similar but smaller King Penguin — around 3 feet tall — breeds on Antarctic islands.

From these giants, penguins range down to the foot-tall Little Blue, or Fairy, Penguin of the southern coasts of Australia and New Zealand.

The largest rookeries on the shores of Antarctica and the Antarctic islands are those of the Adelie Penguin, some of which are estimated to contain a million birds. Males weigh about 13 pounds, females 11 pounds, and they build nests of small stones for their two eggs during the Antarctic spring.

See page 253
The Magellan Penguin of both shores of South America, as far north as southern Brazil and southern Chile, nests in burrows that it excavates itself — or, if the soil is not suitable for a burrow, in a shallow scrape, preferably under a bush.

Penguins kept in warm climates are susceptible to asper-gillosis, a respiratory disease, and to avian malaria. Some com-paratively resistant species may be kept in the open air, however, and the Black-footed (or Jackass) Penguin of the west coast of
See page 253
South Africa, the Humboldt Penguin of the west coast of South America up to Peru, and the crested Rockhopper that winters up the east coast of Buenos Aires are likely to be seen in outdoor aquarium pools, where they dive, "fly" underwater, and oc-casionally even nest and rear their young.

Pelicans
ORDER PELECANIFORMES: PELECANIDAE

"Ungainly" is a fitting word to describe a pelican. However we may admire its expertness at scooping up fish in its great, gaping pouch, its squat body and short legs and outsize webbed feet inevitably provoke a smile. There are six species, and they

live along the coasts and inland waters of the warm and tropical parts of the world.

American White Pelicans, breeding from western Canada to southern Texas and migrating to the Gulf of Mexico and Florida, have the interesting habit of joining together in communal fishing parties. Lining up in a straggling semicircle offshore, they beat the water with their wings as they move toward the shallows, driving small fish before them. It takes about 4 pounds of fish a day to feed an American White Pelican, and those that live in the Great Salt Lake in Utah, where there are no fish, have to fly a considerable distance to feed.

The Eastern Brown Pelican of the Atlantic and Gulf Coasts, the California Brown Pelican, and the Peruvian Brown Pelican are truly marine, and they fish by plunging into the sea with a splashing plop, engulfing a fish, and rising to the surface with the beak held high to drain the water out of the pouch. This is the moment when a wise gull may swoop down and seize the fish before the pelican can swallow it.

Pelicans are sociable birds, nesting together on the ground or in bushes and often flying together in straggling lines or in a well-disciplined V formation. Some white pelicans have a wingspread of 9 feet, the browns about 6½ feet. One to four eggs are laid, which hatch in about twenty-eight days. Even the nestlings have a noticeably heavy pouch, although the beak is short. The parents feed them by regurgitating food, and the young can fly in about two months.

Gannets
PELECANIFORMES: SULIDAE

Sheer sea cliffs and rocky offshore islands are the home of the gannets all around the world except in Antarctica. All dedicated birdlovers know of—and thousands have visited—the gannetries in the Gulf of St. Lawrence and off the Gaspé Peninsula in Canada.

Cliffs and islands are their home only for breeding, however; much of their life is spent on the water. There they sleep, and there they make their plunging dives for fish (a gannet has been netted 90 feet below the surface).

The Northern Gannet, found on both sides of the North Atlantic, is snowy white with black primary feathers in its wings and a touch of pale yellow on its head. In winter it ranges as far south as North Africa and the Gulf of Mexico. The sharply pointed beak is sometimes said to be used to spear fish, but actually the bird swirls under a fish and captures it in its open beak as it rises.

There are nine species of gannet, and the tropical species are known as boobies, a word for dunces or stupid persons, because of the ease with which they can be captured.

Cormorants
PELECANIFORMES: PHALACROCORACIDAE

Cormorants, also known as shags, are voracious eaters of fish, and where there are huge concentrations of them, their nitrogen-rich droppings are collected as fertilizer—in such quantities that cormorants have been called the most valuable birds in the world. They feed mostly on fish of little economic value.

Guanay Cormorants

Double-crested Cormorant

They are coastal birds around the world, breeding on cliffs and crags and islets and sometimes in trees. The plumage of most is dark, giving off a bluish or greenish glint, and the beak ends in a strong hook. They are adept at swimming underwater, to the surprising depth of 100 feet.

Among the approximately thirty species the Common Cormorant has a worldwide distribution, from Labrador and Nova Scotia all around Europe, Africa, and Asia and down to Australia. The related Japanese Cormorant is still used for fishing in Japan; the tethered bird is allowed to dive after a fish and bring it to the surface, but a collar around its neck keeps it from swallowing its prey—which is squeezed out of its mouth by the fisherman.

One of the prettiest of the cormorants is the Double-crested of Alaska to the Bahamas; its head is orange and yellow in the breeding season, ornamented with curling black and white feathers.

The valuable producers of guano, or fertilizer, are the Guanay Cormorant of western South America and the Cape Cormorant of southern Africa. The guano harvesters of South Africa protect the birds and build nesting platforms for them.

Atlantic Puffin diving

Puffins

ORDER CHARADRIIFORMES: ALCIDAE

Puffins—ludicrously heavy-beaked sea birds—belong to a family of twenty-two species with many common names: auk, auklet, murre, murrelet, guillemot, and dovekie. All are sea-cliff nesters in the Northern Hemisphere.

Given an air-conditioned artificial habitat approximating their rocky home, puffins may do well in captivity. Perhaps the most spectacular is the Atlantic Puffin, whose huge beak is mostly bright red in winter; its horny sheath is shed in the fall, and the beak is then smaller and more parrotlike; indeed, puffins are often called "sea parrots." The Atlantic Puffin breeds along the North Atlantic coasts south to Nova Scotia, Maine, and Norway and nests in burrows.

On the Pacific side of North America the Tufted Puffin is found from Alaska to lower Canada. During the breeding season it grows yellow plumes on its head. The Tufted Puffin also nests in burrows excavated in the earth atop sea cliffs and rocky islands. The Horned Puffin of the North Pacific lacks the plumes of the Tufted.

258

MAMMALS

Aquatic mammals are no different from other mammals except that they live entirely or mostly in water—and there are comparatively few kinds: about 136 species against 4,200 species of all mammals. All are warm-blooded, breathe atmospheric air, bring forth their young alive, and nurse them from milk glands.

Most are well known, at least by common name. They include dolphins, porpoises, whales of many kinds, the sea otter, seals, sea lions, walruses, the dugong, and manatees. Some inhabit rivers and river mouths or coastal waters, while others, such as the great whales, roam the deep oceans of the world. In size they range from the 80-pound sea otter to the 120-ton Blue, or Sulphur-bottom, Whale, the largest mammal that has ever lived.

Limited though they are in kinds, their economic importance is great as a source of furs, oil, and meat; indeed, exploitation of some of the whales is still so unremitting that conservationists are alarmed about their future.

Obviously the exhibition of aquatic mammals is limited not only by size but also by feeding habits; those that readily accept fish, clams, squids, and shrimps are most easily kept in captivity.

Dolphins, Porpoises, and Whales
ORDER CETACEA

Cetaceans are the largest order of aquatic mammals, with some ninety species. They are found in every sea and in some rivers and lakes. In general the body is torpedo-shaped, the front limbs have become flippers, there are no hind limbs, and the tail flukes are horizontal, rather than vertical as in a fish. Cetaceans breathe through a single or double blowhole on the top of the head; this closes when they submerge.

Originally land-dwelling animals, they took up life in the sea millions of years ago. Remnants of hair are found on newborn dolphins, usually on the snout, and some freshwater dolphins retain these bristlelike hairs throughout life. Evidence of hind limbs sometimes remains as rudimentary pelvic bones embedded in the skin.

The animals swim by up and down beats of the tail. Under-

water they utter a great variety of sounds that are used for echo-location and to find food—like the ultrasonic "radar" in bats—and perhaps for communication with each other.

Baleen whales, such as the Blue, Finback, and Right Whales, feed on minute aquatic animals such as the shrimplike creatures called krill. Toothed cetaceans take fish, squids, octopuses, and the like; the only exception is the well-named Killer Whale that feeds primarily on warm-blooded animals such as seals, walruses, and penguins. Packs of Killers even kill and eat huge baleen whales.

One young is usual in cetaceans. The baby is born tailfirst in the water and immediately comes to the surface for air.

Freshwater or River Dolphins
CETACEA: PLATANISTIDAE

The Amazon Dolphin of the Amazon and Orinoco river systems of South America attains a length of nearly 10 feet and a weight of about 275 pounds. Young ones are dark above, grayish below, and adults tend to be pinkish or flesh-colored above.

The beak is long, slender, and slightly down-curved. It appears to be used not only for seizing fish but for probing the river bottom for mud-dwelling fishes and crayfish. These dolphins travel singly, in pairs, or in small parties and surface to breathe about every 45 seconds.

Both fresh and coastal waters of South America are the home of the La Plata River Dolphin. It is only about half the length of the Amazon Dolphin, and its habits are similar. There are four species in the family.

OPPOSITE: *Atlantic Bottle-nose Dolphins.* JERRY GREENBERG PHOTO.

White Whale, or Beluga, and Narwhal
CETACEA: MONODONTIDAE

White Whales and Narwhals, the only members of their family, live along the Arctic oceanic coasts and enter the mouths of the larger rivers.

Specimens of the White Whale (also called the Beluga) have been exhibited at the New York Aquarium since 1961 from such widely separated areas as the southern coast of Alaska and the Gulf of St. Lawrence.

A young White Whale is dark gray to almost black, becoming lighter as it matures, until it is almost paper-white at five to ten years. Adult males reach a length of about 17 feet and a weight of nearly 2,000 pounds, females a length of 15 feet. They are hunted in northern waters for oil, meat, and leather and are usually found in pods of up to one hundred.

For the most part they are bottom-feeders on fish, squids, and crustaceans. They can stay under the water without surfacing for air for as long as fifteen minutes, but ordinarily they come up more often; they are known to dive to a depth of nearly 200 feet.

A peculiarity of the Narwhal is its spirally twisted tusk (always twisted from left to right) that may be 9 feet long. Only males have the tusk (which is really a tooth), and although it is not used for fighting, it is suspected that it plays a part in a display ritual. In the Middle Ages the tusk was thought to be the "horn" of the mythical unicorn and to have magical medicinal properties. Narwhal feeding habits are thought to be about the same as those of the White Whale.

No Narwhal had ever been exhibited alive until the summer of 1969 when the New York Aquarium obtained a two-month-old baby from the Canadian Arctic.

Dolphins, Porpoises, and Killer Whales
CETACEA: DELPHINIDAE

This is the largest family of cetaceans, about sixty-two species out of approximately ninety. They inhabit all seas, from the Arctic to Antarctica, and enter the mouths of many large rivers. Some of the dolphins are celebrated for their intelligence and are being intensively studied in captivity.

Killer Whale

The Common Dolphin, about 8 feet long, prefers the warm and temperate seas, and schools of several hundred are often seen playing around ships, shooting through the water at speeds of up to 25 knots and making high leaps out of the water. The usual color is brown or blackish above, white below, with bands of gray, white, and yellow on the sides. Like other dolphins, it feeds on fish, squids, octopuses, and the like.

Perhaps the most famous Risso's Dolphin, or Gray Grampus, was an individual known as "Pelorus Jack" that from sometime in the late 1880's to 1911, 1912, or 1916 (accounts vary) met and accompanied ships in Cook Strait between the two main islands of New Zealand. It is widely believed that whalers shot him (or her).

The dolphin often seen in aquatic shows is likely to be the Atlantic Bottle-nosed Dolphin, which reaches a length of about 12 feet and a weight of more than 400 pounds. It is a playful, inoffensive creature, readily taught simple tricks and well adapted to life in an aquarium because it normally lives in shallow coastal waters. The great variety of its underwater calls has given rise to some rather inconclusive experiments in "communication" between human beings and the dolphins.

The Pacific White-sided Dolphin has also been trained to put on shows, such as making high leaps out of water in unison. It gathers in schools estimated to contain fifteen hundred individuals.

See page 263

The most spectacular member of the family is certainly the Killer Whale, chiefly found in extreme northern and southern seas, but in other oceans as well. It is unmistakable: black above, white below, with a white patch behind the eye. When it swims, its tall dorsal fin projects above the water in a rather sharklike aspect. A big male may be nearly 30 feet long (the average is nearer 20 feet) and weigh more than a ton.

Most members of the family feed on fish, cuttlefish, squids, and the like; the Killer Whale goes in for good red meat—seals, young walruses, other smaller whales, penguins, sea birds—in addition to the usual fare. Schools of Killers will attack even large prey with concerted ferocity, and yet, in captivity they readily take fish from an attendant's hand. An 18-foot specimen in the New York Aquarium ate 180 pounds of fish a day.

Harbor Porpoises, also known as Common Porpoises (and as "Puffing Pigs" in the Bay of Fundy), are true porpoises and the smallest of the cetaceans, adults reaching a length of about 5 feet and a weight of 110 pounds. They like the mouths of rivers and sometimes ascend large streams and at one time were hunted for oil and meat. They are not as playful as most members of the family. Most are black above and white below; some are all black.

Meat Eaters

ORDER CARNIVORA

The carnivores, or meat eaters, include dogs, cats, bears, weasels, and many others, among them the otters. All otters are thoroughly at home in the water, but only two are exclusively marine: the little-known Marine Otter of the Pacific coast of southern South America and the much better known Sea Otter of the North American coast. The latter is the only one that will be discussed here; the freshwater otters are most commonly exhibited in zoological parks.

Sea Otter

CARNIVORA: MUSTELIDAE

Until it was hunted almost to extinction for the sake of its dense, soft fur, the Sea Otter was one of the world's most valuable animals, with an enormous range from Kamchatka and the Aleutians down the Pacific coast to Lower California. Under international protection both Northern and Southern races are making a slow comeback.

The Sea Otter reaches a length of just under 4 feet, exclusive of the tail, and a weight of up to 80 pounds — far more than any freshwater otter. It stays close to the shoreline and is closely associated with beds of kelp, in which it floats on its back and even sleeps. It dives to feed on fish, sea urchins, abalones, crabs, clams, and the like, bringing food to the surface from as deep as 100 feet. To get at the soft interior of shellfish, it floats on its back, a stone resting on its belly, and pounds the shell against the stone.

Northern Sea Otter.
JOSEPH A. DAVIS
PHOTO.

Seals, Sea Lions, Walruses
ORDER PINNIPEDIA

Seacoasts of much of the world are the home of most of the pinnipeds (the word means "wing-footed," referring to the modification of the limbs as flippers), but a few enter rivers or are found in inland lakes. Flippers are efficient in the water, less so on land; thus the pinnipeds spend most of their lives in the water, where they feed chiefly on fish, shellfish, squids, and other kinds of flesh, depending on the species. They all come ashore, on land or ice, to bear their young. One pup is almost invariably the rule. The breeding colonies are often enormous.

Apart from man, who hunts many of them for meat, oil, and furs, their chief enemies are the Polar Bear, sharks, the Killer Whale, the Leopard Seal, and the Walrus.

Pinnipeds are found in all seas except the northern Indian Ocean, but there are more kinds, and more individuals, in the extreme northern and southern oceans.

Sea Lions and Fur Seals
PINNIPEDIA: OTARIIDAE

The twelve species of sea lion and fur seal live along the coasts of western North America, both coasts of South America, and around southern Africa, Australia, New Zealand, and a few oceanic islands. Estimates of their numbers range from 2,850,000 to 4,176,000.

Next to the Northern Fur Seal the South American Sea Lion is the most plentiful, with an estimated 700,000 to 1,000,000. Males reach a length of about 8 feet and a weight of 1,100 pounds. They are not seriously exploited for hides and meat, mostly because they live along almost inaccessible shores.

The largest member of the family is the Steller's Sea Lion of southern California north to the Aleutians; an old male may be more than 11 feet long and weigh 2,000 pounds. Males fight viciously for territory and harems in the breeding season and usually bear deep scars.

The sea lion commonly seen in aquariums, zoos, and circuses is the California Sea Lion that lives along the Pacific coast from Mexico to British Columbia. Herds haul up on shore in May or June, and single pups are born at that time, the young dabbling in shallow water until they learn to catch fish and to swim. Even an old bull, or "beachmaster," weighs only about 600 pounds; females are a third of that weight.

One of the brightest pages in the history of conservation is contributed by the Northern Fur Seal, whose most famous breeding grounds are in the Pribilof Islands in the Bering Sea. By 1910 hunting for furs had reduced the species to about 132,000 animals. International treaties signed in 1911 and renewed in 1957 gave time for the herds to rebuild by controlling hunting for fur, oil, and meat, so that the population has increased to an estimated 1,580,000 to 1,920,000; now only bachelor bulls and surplus females may be taken each year. The Northern Fur Seal has a definite migration pattern and in winter moves south along the Canadian coast and into Japanese waters. Some may cover 6,000 miles in one year.

There are believed to be 300,000 to 600,000 South African Fur Seals and 80,000 to 200,000 South American Fur Seals; the latter is harvested by controlled hunting for furs and oil. *Steller's Sea Lion*

Atlantic Walrus

Walruses
PINNIPEDIA: ODOBENIDAE

Riding ice floes or swimming in the almost-freezing waters high in the Arctic Circle, Walruses are the giants of the northern seascape; an old male may weigh 3,000 pounds, and a female 2,000 pounds. There may be as many as a hundred in a herd lying on the ice shelf, although large concentrations are growing rarer because of wasteful hunting by the Eskimos, and the world population of the two races, Atlantic and Pacific, is now estimated at only forty-five to ninety thousand. It will be a sad day for the Eskimos if Walruses all but disappear, for they use every part of the animal—hide, blubber, bones, tusks, tendons.

In feeding, Walruses sink to the bottom to a depth of perhaps 300 feet and use their tusks to dredge up shellfish, which they crush or suck open to get at the soft parts. Both sexes have tusks, but the male's are larger and are sometimes a yard long. Both sexes also have heavy, stiff "walrus moustaches" formed of some four hundred bristles.

Earless, or Hair, Seals
PINNIPEDIA: PHOCIDAE

The Earless Seals—which means merely that they have no external ears—are most numerous in the cold seas of both hemispheres, but some live in temperate or tropical waters, or peculiarly, in freshwater lakes. The world population is estimated at 10,887,000 to 22,142,000.

Most are covered with rather stiff hairs and lack the soft underfur of the fur seals, so that the economic value of northern species is chiefly as a source of food, oil, and clothing for the Eskimos. They cannot turn the hind flippers forward, and on land they travel by an awkward wriggling and hunching; nevertheless, some can make considerable speed.

Fish, shellfish, krill, and squids are eaten by most, although the Leopard Seal of Antarctica preys on warm-blooded creatures such as penguins and other sea birds and other seals.

Seals in the polar regions, living under ice, keep breathing holes free by biting an opening in new ice.

The Harbor Seal is often seen along the coasts on both sides of the North Atlantic and North Pacific, especially in the autumn when breeding groups gather in sheltered waters. Some occasionally wander as far south as the New York area. Average weight is 200 to 300 pounds.

Newborn Harbor Seal pups are covered with soft white or yellowish wool, which is usually shed before birth or very soon afterward; the adult coat is yellowish or brown, with darker patches.

The Ringed Seal lives around the world in the North Polar regions and is an important source of food, oil, and skins for the Eskimos. It is small—only about 250 pounds, the smallest of the pinnipeds—and gets its common name from the mottled pattern of white rings on its dark back. This is a very common seal, and the world population is estimated at 2,267,000 to 5,815,000.

A close relative is the small Baikal Seal, landlocked in the mile-deep Lake Baikal of Siberia, 1,500 miles from the sea. There are believed to be 40,000 to 100,000 of them. Another, and more abundant, relative is the Caspian Seal, whose herds, totaling 800,000 to 1,500,000, move north to the ice on the Caspian Sea in winter.

One of the rarer seals is the Ribbon Seal of the Bering, Siberian, and Okhotsk seas, prettily marked with light bands around the neck, each foreflipper, and the rump. It does not gather in large herds and so is seldom taken except by Eskimos, who prize it for its decorative pelt.

Another boldly marked seal is the Harp Seal of North Atlantic and Arctic waters. Grayish in general color, it has a vaguely harp-shaped dark marking across the back and down the sides. There are three huge groups: 1,000,000 to 1,500,000 in the White Sea, 500,000 to 1,000,000 in the Greenland Sea, and 3,000,000 to 4,500,000 around Newfoundland and the Gulf of St. Lawrence. Although the seal's scientific name means "ice-lover," it is much more likely to be found in open water than on ice, except when the pups are being born. The seals then keep open the natural holes in thick ice as escape hatches in case of attack.

For many years Gray Seals have been a storm center in the British Isles, condemned by fishermen for their feeding habits and defended by conservationists. There are two other populations, one mostly in the Gulf of St. Lawrence and another in the Baltic Sea. Adult males reach a length of 9 feet and a weight of 650 pounds. There is no denying that Gray Seals feed on fish, including valuable species such as salmon, halibut, and flounder, but they take many "trash fish" as well. Young seals have been caught at a depth of 500 feet. The pelage is gray and strongly mottled, and the seal has a rather long, doglike face.

Next to the gigantic Elephant Seal the Bearded Seal of the North Polar seas is the largest member of the family, up to about 1,000 pounds. It gets its common name from its luxuriant beard of long bristles. The Bearded Seal has great curiosity about any unusual sight or sound and makes little attempt to escape an enemy, so it is easily killed. The world population is believed to be 75,000 to 150,000.

There are three species of Monk Seal, one of which is probably extinct, and they live in such widely separated areas as the Mediterranean, the Caribbean, and around Hawaii. Except for the Northern Elephant Seal they are the only pinnipeds that are entirely at home in tropical waters.

The Mediterranean Monk Seal was much more plentiful two thousand years ago than it is now — there are believed to be only one to five thousand of them — and they were commonly hunted, towns were named after them, and they appeared on coins. They weigh an average of about 500 pounds and are either a uniform brown above or grayish or yellowish with black spots.

The Caribbean Monk Seal was almost hunted out of existence by 1885 and was last recorded around Jamaica in 1952. The animal was exhibited in the New York Aquarium in 1897 and again in 1909; the specimens had the not-so-engaging habits of spitting water at visitors or splashing them with sweeps of their flippers.

Only one thousand to fifteen hundred Hawaiian Monk Seals still exist, under protection, on a few of the Hawaiian atolls. They were slaughtered for skins and oil in the last century until they were almost extinct and hunting became unprofitable.

There is little likelihood that the Crabeater Seal will soon become extinct, however; its world population is an estimated two to five million. It lives among the drifting ice in Antarctica and is not hunted commercially. Its summer coat is snowy white, and it molts to a mottled grayish brown.

The Crabeater Seal (which does *not* feed on crabs, but on krill and small fish) breeds along the edge of the pack ice. On ice or snow it is extremely fast and can outdistance a running man.

See page 273

Less well known is the Ross Seal from the fringe of the

TOP: *Southern Elephant Seals.* R. L. PENNEY PHOTO.
BOTTOM: *Crabeater Seal.* CARLETON RAY PHOTO.

Antarctic continent; there are believed to be only twenty to fifty thousand of them. They are greenish gray above, with yellowish stripes on the sides, and lighter below. They probably reach a length of about 11 feet.

The seal that regularly preys on warm-blooded animals — penguins, other sea birds, other seals — is the Leopard Seal of the Antarctic and sub-Antarctic seas. Males are about 10 feet long, and females, oddly, some 2 feet longer. Both have a rather long and narrow body and can open the heavily armed mouth in an enormous gape; the reptilian appearance of the animal has often been remarked. On land they move with a looping action somewhat reminiscent of a caterpillar. Their usual method of attacking a penguin in the water is to come up under it, seize it, shake it above water in a shower of feathers, and then consume it.

The Antarctic continent itself is the home of the Weddell Seal, the most southerly of any seal. It is dark above, light below, and reaches a weight of about 900 pounds and a length of 10 feet for males, 11 feet for females. During the Antarctic spring and summer Weddell Seals bask on the ice near an escape hole into the water—usually a hole that they have bitten out of the ice. In winter they go under the ice and come to blowholes for air or use domes of air trapped by the ice. They are highly vocal animals, both on land (they belch, gurgle, and moan constantly) and under the water; expeditions from the New York Aquarium have made elaborate studies of their underwater sounds.

There are believed to be 200,000 to 500,000 Weddell Seals; they are not commercially hunted.

The Hooded, or Bladdernose, Seal lives among the pack ice in the high North Atlantic and Arctic seas—although, surprisingly, it occasionally wanders far south and has been sighted off Florida. Bulls are grayish blue above, light below, and reach a length of 11 feet 6 inches; females are slightly smaller. Their distinguishing feature is the inflatable hood on top of the head; when it is blown up, as when the animal is angry or excited, it forms a large red bladder.

Elephant Seals are well named. An old bull of the Southern Elephant Seal may be 22 feet long and weigh 8,000 pounds, and it is "adorned" with a trunklike proboscis up to 15 inches long,

Ross Seal.
CARLETON RAY
PHOTO.

through which it trumpets, snorts, roars, puffs, and sighs. The hood is at maximum size only during the breeding season; females do not have a well-developed trunk.

See page 271

The Southern Elephant Seal ranges around the world in sub-Antarctic waters and was relentlessly hunted for oil until the end of the last century; there are perhaps 380,000 to 660,000 today.

There are far fewer Northern Elephant Seals, a species only slightly smaller than the Southern. It breeds along the coasts of California and Lower California, and there are some eight to ten thousand. Elephant Seals are agile enough in the water, despite their great bulk, but hunch along awkwardly on land. They like to lie on a beach, puffing and snorting and snoring, often half across another member of the herd. They show little fear of human beings, and a man can walk among them, merely arousing a chorus of snorts before they go back to sleep. Both the Northern and Southern Elephant Seals have the habit of throwing sand over themselves by movements of their flippers.

The Northern Elephant Seal was hunted almost to extinction by the 1860's, for it was a good producer of oil, but it is now making a slow comeback under protection.

Dugong and Manatees
ORDER SIRENIA

There are only four living species in this order, two in the Old World and two in the New World. All are exclusively aquatic and never leave the water, but one is found only in fresh water, one only in salt water, and the other two are equally at home in salt, brackish, and fresh water. They are vegetarians and feed on water plants.

The name of the order refers to the mythological Sirens, mermaids who were sometimes pictured as holding their infants out of the water to nurse. Dugongs were once believed to nurse their young in that manner, but this is apparently not so. Probably the young nurse underwater, as young manatees do.

A fifth species, Steller's Sea Cow, once lived in the Bering Sea, but was exterminated in the eighteenth century.

Dugong
SIRENIA: DUGONGIDAE

The Dugong lives in the Red Sea and along the shores of the Indian Ocean, south to Madagascar and east to the Marshall Islands. It is a heavy-bodied animal, averaging 8 to 10 feet long and weighing 600 pounds or more. The forelimbs are paddlelike, there are no hind limbs, and the tail is crescentic. Dugongs have seldom been exhibited.

Manatees
SIRENIA: TRICHECHIDAE

Manatees differ most noticeably from the Dugong by having a rounded tail. Adults propel themselves underwater by powerful strokes of the tail, but the young swim with their flippers.

There are three species, varying somewhat in size but all uniformly dark gray to black.

The 7- to 12-foot American Manatee lives along the Atlantic coast from North Carolina to Florida and the Gulf of Mexico and through the West Indies to northern South America. It often enters slow-flowing streams and in British Guiana has been used to clear waterweeds out of canals. The animal is protected in Florida and is often seen in the Everglades and even inside the city limits of Miami. Where there is no protection, manatees are hunted for their excellent meat and for oil and leather.

The Amazonian Manatee is slightly smaller than the American Manatee and lives only in the fresh waters of the Amazon basin.

The African Manatee is a coastal species of western Africa from Senegal to Angola and also enters large rivers.

Born underwater, young manatees are immediately brought to the surface by the mother. They nurse underwater for the first eighteen months.

Amazon Manatees of the Amazon and Orinoco drainage systems of South America

INDEX

Scientific names are followed by the heading under which the common name will be found. **Bold Face** refers to illustrations.

B

Badis (*Badis badis*), 148
Badis badis (Badis), 148
Bagre marinus (Catfish), 68, **69**
Balanus eburneus (Barnacle), 231; *nubilus* (Barnacle), 231
Balistes capriscus (Triggerfish), 190, **191**; *vetula* (Triggerfish), **189**, 190
Balistidae, 188
Balistoides conspicillum (Triggerfish), **189**, 190
Barb, Black Ruby (*Barbus nigrofasciatus*), **67**; Blind (*Caecobarbus geertsi*), **62**, 63
Barbus nigrofasciatus (Barb), **67**
Barnacle, Acorn, 231; Atlantic Common (*Balanus eburneus*), 231; Giant (*Balanus nubilus*), 231; Goose (*Lepas anatifera*), **230**, 231
Barracuda, Great (*Sphyraena barracuda*), **185**; Northern (*Sphyraena borealis*), 185
Basket Star (*Gorgonocephalus agassizi*), 222, **223**
Bass, Black Sea (*Centropristes striatus*), 4, 107; Channel, **130**, 131; Largemouth (*Micropterus salmoides*), 114, **116**; Smallmouth (*Micropterus dolomieui*), 114, **117**; Striped (*Morone saxatilis*), **104**
Batrachoididae, 195
Beaugregory (*Eupomacentrus leucostictus*), 157
Bêche-de-mer, 226
Belonidae, 81
Beluga (*Huso huso*), 39; (mammal), **262**
Betta splendens (Fighting Fish), 184
Bichir, Congo (*Polypterus weeksi*), 38
Bigeye (*Priacanthus arenatus*), 111, **112**
Billfish, 82
Bitterling (*Rhodeus sericeus*), 62
Bivalvia, 238
Blenniidae, 180
Blennius tentacularis (Blenny), **181**
Blenny, Fringehead (*Blennius tentacularis*), **181**
Blowfish, **193**
Bluefish (*Pomatomus saltatrix*), 119, **120**
Bluegill (*Lepomis macrochirus*), 111, **113**
Bluehead (*Thalassoma bifasciatum*), 161, **162**
Bodianus rufus (Hogfish), 163, **165**
Bonefish (*Albula vulpes*), 43, 44
Bothidae, 186
Botia macracanthus (Loach), 66, **67**
Bowfin (*Amia calva*), **40**
Boxfish, Spiny (*Chilomycterus schoepfi*), 195, **196**
Brevoortia tyrannus (Menhaden), 44
Brittle Star, Daisy (*Ophipholis aculeata*), 222; Long-armed (*Amphipholis squamata*), 221, **222**
Buffalo, Bigmouth (*Ictiobus cyprinellus*), 65; Smallmouth (*Ictiobus bubalus*), **66**
Bullhead, Black (*Ictalurus melas*), 72; Brown (*Ictalurus nebulosus*), **71**, 72, **73**; Yellow (*Ictalurus natalis*), 72

Butterfish (*Peprilus triacanthus*), 183
Butterflyfish, Barred (*Chaetodon multicinctus*), **147**; Foureye (*Chaetodon capistratus*), **143**; Fourspot (*Chaetodon quadrimaculatus*), **144**; Long-nosed (*Forcipiger longirostris*), **142**, 144; Raccoon (*Chaetodon lunula*), 144; Spotfin (*Chaetodon ocellatus*), 143
By-the-Wind Sailor (*Velella velella*), **207**

C

Caecobarbus geertsi (Barb), **62**, 63
Calappa flammea (Crab), 236
Callinectes sapidus (Crab), 235
Callorhinus ursinus cynocephalus (Seal), 266
Campostoma anomalum (Stoneroller), 62
Carangidae, 120
Caranx hippos (Jack), **121**
Carapidae, 182
Carapus bermudensis (Pearlfish), 182, 226
Carassius auratus (Goldfish), 62, **64**
Carcharhinidae, 27
Carcharhinus obscurus (Shark), **25**
Carcharias oxyrinchus (Shark), 26; *taurus*, **22**, 23
Carchariidae, 23
Carcharodon carcharias (Shark), 24, **26**
Caretta caretta (Loggerhead), 246, **248**
Carnegiella marthae (Hatchetfish), 58
Carp (*Cyprinus carpio*), **63**
Carybdea alata (Sea Wasp), 209
Cassiopeia (*Cassiopeia xamachana*), **206**, 209
Cassiopeia xamachana (Cassiopeia), **206**, 209
Catalufa, 111
Catfish, Blue (*Ictalurus furcatus*), **71**, 72; Channel (*Ictalurus punctatus*), 72; Congo Eel (*Channallabes apus*), 74; Congo Upside-down (*Synodontis nigriventris*), 74, **75**; Electric (*Malapterurus electricus*), 77, **78**; Flathead (*Pylodictis olivaris*), **70**; Gafftopsail (*Bagre marinus*), 68, **69**; Marine (*Plotosus anguillaris*), 70, **72**; Mississippi, **71**, 72; Sea (*Galeichthys felis*), **68**; Walking, 74, **76**; West African Eel (*Gymnallabes typus*), 74
Catostomidae, 65
Catostomus commersoni (Sucker), **65**
Cave Fish, Blind (*Astyanax jordani*), **54**, **56**
Cavefish, Northern (*Amblyopsis spelaea*), 98; Ozark (*Amblyopsis rosae*), 98; Southern (*Typhlichthys subterraneus*), 98; Spring (*Chologaster agassizi*), 98
Centrarchidae, 111
Centriscidae, 89
Centriscus strigatus (Shrimpfish), 89, **90**
Centropomidae, 102
Centropomus undecimalis (Snook), 102
Centropristes striatus (Bass), 4, 107
Centropyge potteri (Angelfish), 144, **147**

T